THE OFFICIAL GUIDE TO

CRINKLEY BOTTOM

Noel Edmonds and John Machin

Illustrated by Mark Pasterfield

FANTAIL

FANTAIL BOOKS

Published by the Penguin Group
Penguin Books Ltd, 27 Wrights Lane, London W8 5TZ, England
Penguin Books USA Inc., 375 Hudson Street, New York, New York 10014, USA
Penguin Books Australia Ltd, Ringwood, Victoria, Australia
Penguin Books Canada Ltd, 10 Alcorn Avenue, Toronto, Ontario, Canada M4V 3B2
Penguin Books (NZ) Ltd, 182–190 Wairau Road, Auckland 10, New Zealand

Penguin Books Ltd, Registered Offices: Harmondsworth, Middlesex, England

First published 1993

1 3 5 7 9 10 8 6 4 2

Fantail Film and TV Tie-in edition first published 1993

Made and printed in Great Britain by William Clowes Limited, Beccles and London

Inside photographs: Hulton Deutsch

Contents

Foreword

There's always been a little Bottom in my life. The itinerant Edmonds family have formerly resided in Piggotts bottom, Wally's Bottom, Pratts Bottom and now Crinkley Bottom. Of all the Bottoms, however, it is only the latter which has secured my affections – indeed, my heart is in my Crinkley Bottom. Of course it's been a hard struggle to become accepted as a local. It seems the Saturday night parties at the Great House have been the subject of much speculation and rumour. If only the villagers had television sets, then they would understand that it's still possible to have a really wild time and keep your clothes on.

Still, I mustn't complain. The villagers may have a better feel for their Bottom than I do, but the peace and tranquillity of this rural oasis is unique in our modern hi-tech world. I hope this Guide won't cause too much intrusion into the sleepy, comatose, unconscious hamlet that is Crinkley Bottom. If the book does stir your juices and you feel the wanderlust rising in your spleen do please drive slowly through the village, don't park on the grass and don't leave your bags unattended (Crinkley Bottom menfolk are desperate!).

The babbling brook will serenade you, the humming bees will tranquillize you, the roadside banks of wild meadow flowers will intoxicate you and the sun-kissed rolling pastures will beckon you onwards. Oh, and don't forget to drop in at the Great House for tea and muffins. I might even be able to rustle up one of Pru's imploded crumpets. Enjoy this Guide, hopefully fall in love with this wonderful part of Olde England, and have a warm feeling about my Crinkley Bottom.

Map of Crinkley Bottom

To Eff Hall-on-the-Hill 6 miles

Firkers Wood

Tinklers

Stream

To Tinkling-in-the-bog 3 miles

Tinkling away

Wiggley Woggle Wood

Muckflirters Meadow

Oblong Square

Nibblers Nook

The Venus De Milo Arms

Crinkley Castle

Tiddlers Lake

School

Tenderpart Court

Snogging Bind

Bottom Lane

Post Office

The bogg

Battle of Crinclium
X 1397

Crinkley Bottom
~ Crinclium ~

Village Green and Playing Field

Church Street

Edmonds Alley

Newt Fielders Walk

Liszt & Newt Inn

Gunge Way

St Bottoms Church

Old Post Office

Mortuary Road

Winking Nun Inn

Naffall Way

Windmill

Fish Inn

The Blooming Leg Inn

Derry Derry

Scrag End

Station

Blobby Falls

Gobbit Bog

Waters Tench Farm

To Nether Scratching 1¾ miles

Naffall Wood

Crinkley Cutting

Hampton Rise

RIVER CRINKLE

To Naffall To Sea 3 miles

N

CARTER

To Little Browning on the Hummock 1¼ miles

Scale of Three inches to One Statute Mile

½ Mile

Copyright Reserved

To Littlewick-on-the-Rise 3 miles

Great House Plan

1. Under-Butler's Rude Carrot Pantry

2. Tradesmen's Entrance (incl. trapdoor to moat)

3. Noel's Nursery (aka The Bawl Room)

4. Mr Blobby's First Aid Room

5. Nibbling Room

6. Haunted Sock Drawer

7. Maid Gooser's Staircase

8. Great Hall Mirror (scene of Noel's first kiss)

9. Noel's Music Room (aka The Whine Cellar)

10. Fan Mail Room (unused since 1977)

11. Wind Tunnel

12. Kitchens (as featured in the I–Spy Book of Insects)

13. Edward VII slept here (during a conversation with Pru)

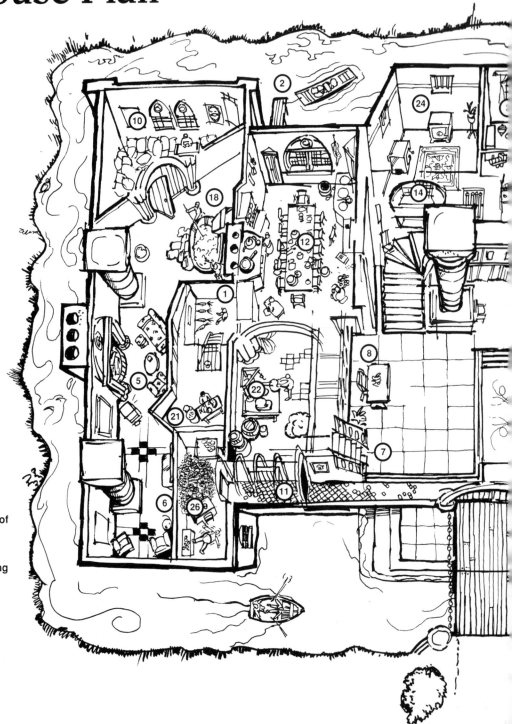

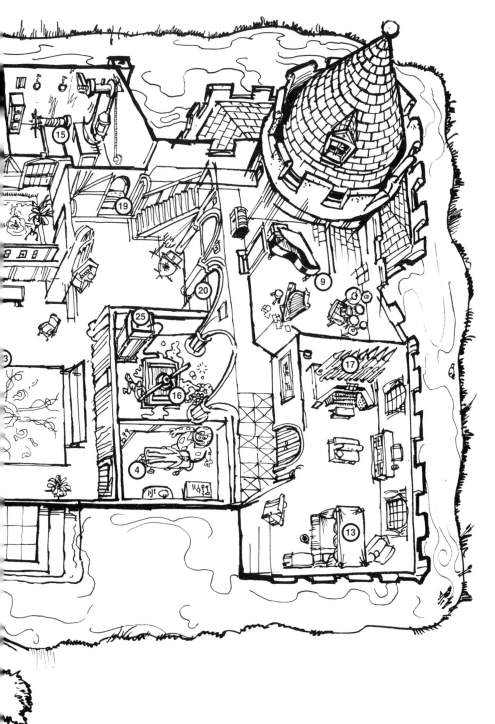

14. Noel's Pullover Cupboard
(extensions built Xmas '89,
Xmas '90, Xmas '91, etc.)

15. Torture Chamber
(incl. rack, iron maiden, and
Noel's old TV scripts)

16. Gunge Press

17. Pru's Organ

18. Porridge Room

19. The Famous Secret Passage

20. Bunion's Passage

21. Crushed Nut Alcove

22. Lard Folding Room

23. Great Hall

24. 31st Wallet Room

25. Gunge Tank

26. Baked Bean Pantry

1. Around Crinkley Bottom

'If sight-seeing were the product of an evolutionary chromosome in the human anatomy, Crinkley Bottomers would soon find themselves being born with only one eye.' – The words of Dangley End philosopher and cult plumber Derek Jung, a distant relation of the other great-thinking primate, Mighty Joe Jung. And, like his ancestor, he was talking a lot of bananas.

There are more things to see in Crinkley Bottom than you can shake a Japanese tourist's photography bill at. As a visitor once put it: see Venice and die, see Crinkley Bottom and wish you were dead. No one was quite sure what he meant, but we think it must've been a compliment. Crinkley Bottom's not the sort of place you can insult easily.

We've got it all here. And more. Sheep, hills, puddles, sheep, sky, stones, trees, sheep, hedgehogs, wellingtons, hedgehogs stuck to wellingtons, sheep, grass, those mini-tombstone things you get by the side of the road, sheep, walls, crisp packets, sheep – oh, and word has it we've even got a few people. Or was that sheep? But look, I've a couple of months before the paper boy delivers last January's *Crinkley Bottom Observer*: why don't I drive you around the place? Well, come on, grab your leather helmet and goggles! There's no hanging about in Crinkley Bottom, you know. Not with the sort of smells we've got coming off the fields round here.

Down the drive from the Great House: it's a bit bumpy, but we'd be here all day if I actually tried driving round the sheep. Slowing for the end of my entrance, and there's the first major tourist attraction: a road sign, so-called because it informs villagers that this is a road.

A quick shimmy, and we're crossing Crinkley Bridge, which was built and rebuilt eight times in the eighteenth century, before villagers realized it should actually go over the river.

Beneath us slops the lazy River Crinkle, swirling in slow syrupy green loops, as it puzzles whether it should flow out to sea or head back up the mountain. It was via the Crinkle in pre-motorized days that villagers transported their harvested grain in heavy hemp sacks. Progress came, and now they put them in boats first.

Off the bridge now and waiting to turn into Dangley Road South. Go on, missus! There used to be a toll booth at this point. It was set up in 1812 to exact a levy off travellers wishing to enter Crinkley Bottom. It went bust in 1813.

At this hour of day, this is a singularly delightful part of Crinkley Bottom. The sun's just rising over the neck of Terry Nutter's dog, and the birds are already up and nailed to the trees, humming the dawn chorus. The atmosphere's fresh, sparkling, tingly; you can sense nature stretching and rubbing the sleep from its eyes. Pity it's almost half-three in the afternoon.

Third gear and – look out, woman! – on the left here, the Crinkley Bottom micro-mini-bus is picking up a clot of a dozen villagers – or the population, as they're known locally. On the right there, by the roadworks, the village idiot's showing off by walking with alternate legs. He's been lifting up the traffic cones, trying to find out which one the little ball's hidden under.

Look out of your left window now, because Snogging Bint Lane's coming up on the right. That brings us coincidentally to Crinkley Bottom's other, slightly less frequented entertainment centre – the Pitz Theatre and Cinema. There's quite a queue outside this afternoon: they must be showing a Sylvester Stallone movie – at the Dangley End Gaumont. Oh! and there's the Crinkley Bottom busker, strumming his cap and passing round an acoustic guitar. Funny thing is, he makes a blooming fortune.

This is Funsville, the leisure district of Crinkley Bottom. And the same to you, mate! After work, villagers flock here to enjoy themselves, and flock home again when they find they have to pay for it. Apart from the Pitz, it comprises Crinkley Bottom Park (located, owing to a slight planning error, in Nether Scratching), the bingo hall, the swimming pool (Liszt and Newt regulars strictly forbidden), and the gymnasium – on the right, there, see? – where the local Athletics Club are warming up after training. And just past them is the library, whose portals intellectual maverick Tosh Scrivener, graduate in Illegal Parties at Crinkleyshire University, is broaching, no doubt to do a spot of research under their helpfully titled 'Books' section.

We're coming up to the lights by the George Inn (built at the end of the last century in Crinkley Bottom, circa 1793). Ahead of us, the main road runs to Dangley End. Well, that's not strictly true: like most things going to Dangley End, it uses a sort of doomed reluctant crawl. But we're turning right – all right, all right, I'm going! – into Cobbler's Lane, named after the local shoe repairer, Albert Lane.

This is a busy thoroughfare, with people almost in double figures. There's the village idiot again, bumping into himself. Elsie Dee, the digital watchmaker, is gesturing to us. I think she's trying to say she's hurt her index finger. And there's the famous bird protectionist and acronym Horace Peebey. Where did he get that face?

A thimbleful of petrol further on and, from  the cryogenic stillness and Toepoker Park-like silence, you can tell we've entered the local industrial sector. The area which put the dated in dilapidated, Crinkley Bottom's industry has gone to the wall – only to find Crinkley Bottom's graffiti wrights have got there first. The brickwork's infested with the stuff around here; just look at it all:

Horace Peebey and pigeon
(Horace is the one on the left)

Beaver-infested rivers are just one dam thing after another.
Fight aggression.
Polar – the atmosphere with a hole in it.
Illiteratacy is nothing to write home about.
I think, therefore, I, er ... need a headache tablet.
Industrial espionage is the mugger of invention.
Love means never having to say your prayers.
The trouble with death is, you're so stiff the day afterwards.
My dictionary duzzn't whirrk.
Model T Fords aren't as black as they're painted.
Pass the buck – play football with a dead rabbit.
Goliath took a dive.
Stop polar bears dying – hide their peroxide bottles.

I wonder how many aerosols it took to do that. And what did they use to write it with?

7

This isn't a complete hive of – look! either cross the road or get back on the pavement, lady! – inactivity. With increasing interest in healthy foods, a vegetarian abattoir has opened. And from that chlorophyll-splattered building nearby, two clever, highly inventive and imaginative villagers are operating an advertising agency called – well, they haven't managed to think up a name for it yet.

Hello, there's a bell clanging. The traffic's pulled over to one side of the road. Just time for a mint – help yourself – before they realize it's the Crinkley Bottom Junior High School bell, and there's no fire engine ... Nine minutes fifty-eight, fifty-nine – Right! we're off again. Now, the school must be around here somewhere – yes, there's the tell-tale lost glove in the school entrance. The cheery, rosy-cheeked local kiddies are teeming out at the end of another fulfilling school day. Put that brick down, sunshine. Yes, and you! Heck, it's the Deputy Head.

A Crinkley Bottom child's mind is a wonderful thing: it starts working the moment he wakes up, and doesn't stop until he gets into school. None the less, Crinkley Bottom Junior High boasts a tradition of excellence in Ancient History. Not surprising really, as most kids around here have direct personal experience of it.

But that's about as far as academic achievement among the pupils goes. Terry Nutter's lad's so bad at Biology, he gets earache in his feet. Maths is a closed book to the three Frizzett twins. And the standard of spelling among scholars and ex-scholars alike is nuthern shawrt uv disgraysfull. Two thirds of them seem to think the three Rs stand for Rabbiting, Rioting and Ram-raiding; the other half's idea of adventure is going on a Duke of Edinburgh Scheme to get up before eight a.m.

Not that things were much different in my day. It's thirt— Where do you think you are, pal – Silverstone? Must be the Geography master – twenty years since I was last here. But, looking around the playground now, with its poison-tipped barbed wire and Black Forest wolf patrol, it's clear the kids haven't really changed; still the same old stereotypes.

There's the Big Hairy Baritone, who's apparently been put through puberty privately at the age of six. He sits at the back, playing with his conkers; and he must be pretty awful at games, because the PE mistress keeps asking to see him after school.

The Runt's there: he's the one with the scarf welded around his throat, and a doctor's note excusing him from school dinners. He hides in his pencil-case at playtime, and his best friend's a hot-water bottle.

There's the Bully with the coconut where his head should be. He fights like a cross between an Olympic freestyle champion and a Mississippi paddle-steamer. His entire private life is spent in detention, and he only comes to school to hand in the lines he hasn't done and to steal the Headmaster's dinner money. In Crinkley Bottom, he's the one who usually goes on to become Council Treasurer.

Then there's the Farmer's Son, with wild tangly hair and teeth to match, who blows bubbles out of his nose every time he laughs.

Mustn't leave out the Duffer, who keeps forgetting to copy his homework. He's having special lessons on how to unfold his arms. His ambition is to leave school and own his own spider. Everyone's got a soft spot for the Duffer because, no matter how badly you did in the exams, he's always done worse.

Finally, there's the Mystery Kid, who turns up half-way through term and sits silently on his own in a corner, while the other kids use him as an ink pellet target. He disappears, dappled in tear stains and Quink blots, a week later, never to be seen again. It's not until three years after you've left that you discover he was the School Inspector.

Happy days, but nostalgia has no place in Crinkley Bottom, when there's so much of the past going on around us in the present. And while we're on the subject, I'm just going to take a sharp right here, welly it past Upper Bottom, and take you around our main residential area, East Bottom. Historically speaking, this is Crinkley Bottom's Palaeolithic sector. We call it the new bit.

Evolution, slower than a monk's hormones in other parts of the village, appears to have jumped into reverse here. Outwardly, the area appears clean and well lit. But the lack of litter is due to generations of knuckles being dragged along the pavements; and the lampposts are only close together so that EastBottomers can swing along between them on their way to gather berries.

The typical EastBottomer is an ugly brute: gruff, ungainly, verandah-browed, shaped like a pea on a snooker triangle. He's still got primordial soup stains down his shirt, and he thinks posture's something cattle graze on. He's a bit like an Australian without the charm.

When the methane cloud clears, you'll be able to see the houses here: mock-Bedrock semis, with three floors – one at the bottom; two at the top. East Bottom homes are a popular tourist attraction. Visitors regularly gather around them in beads and kaftans to celebrate the summer solstice.

Deeper into East Bottom now, past the Flint Tool Hire Shop (Opening Soon): the mammals are gaining a foothold, and the ice sheets are beginning to retreat. Here stands the famous Great Fence of Crinkley Bottom, the only man-made object visible from the Moon (or indeed any other local public house). This remarkable phenomenon was built by primitive villagers around 1066 in Bottom Lane. They were going to built it around 1068, but the neighbours objected.

We're now approaching the end of Bottom Lane, and braking for the customary hold-up: fifteen artics wedged bumper to bumper. This isn't a traffic jam: it's the lorries collecting last night's empties from the Liszt and Newt. There's a short cut, but it's the long way around, so I'll just squeeze – tuck your vest in, madam – through. Phew! talk about narrow streets. Don't worry about the paint on the pavement here, by the way: it's just that they couldn't fit both double white lines in the road.

As we pick up speed down the hill from the L 'n' N, you'll doubtless have come to appreciate the historical importance of Crinkley Bottom. The Government originally planned to site the British Museum here, until they realized Crinkley Bottom actually is the British Museum. And like a museum, there's plenty to see.

Across the way, a little old gent who's spent the morning in conversation with Fanny Smalls at the sub-post office is just being towed away by an RAC van. And there's the village idiot again, in a phone box, telephoning everyone to see if there've been any wrong numbers for him. Over on your left, the village newsagent is taking delivery of 700 copies of the *Crinkley Bottom*

Observer. Fool! He'll never read all those before closing time.

Indicating left, whoops! right – OK, OK, how much road do you want, fella? – and into Church Street. Villagers pulled a subtle double bluff and built a church here: St Bottom's. There it crouches, its spire soaring skywards, sharp as a needle, and almost as long; its stained glass windows twinkling like stained glass windows; its parish noticeboard, empathizingly wooden, proclaiming 'A God is not just for Christmas'.

Crinkley Bottom is a religious community, and congregations are up on Sundays – usually about fifteen minutes after the service is due to start. But the Reverend Dews is worried about support for his organ: he thinks it's dropping off. Things weren't helped in June when the Church Fête had to be cancelled owing to the weather – everyone was too busy sunbathing to go.

Nevertheless, St Bottom's churchyard is doing a lively trade. Situated along Mortuary Road (Crinkley Bottom's dead end), it boasts such illustrious local residents as Tommy 'Jug-Handles' Squirter, hero of the Great Crinkley Bottom Coathanger Shortage; Bill Follows, founder member of the Loners' Club; Gipsy Woes Lee, the misfortune teller with a speech impediment; Trumper Reagan, who claimed he once understood a television lager advert; Gladys Dangley, such an archetypal Crinkley Bottomer, she was born with instructions on how to breathe, but obviously lost them; Porky Charlton, who was so short-sighted, Crinkley Bottomers kept mistaking him for someone else; and Professor Miss Peaky Parton, the double-breasted jacket examiner, who proved not only that time machines were possible, but that they already existed in the form of a one-way ticket to Crinkley Bottom.

Ooh, look! what a stroke of luck. There's the Reverend Dews himself. Talk of the devil. See him – three feet behind those teeth? He's walking in the church grounds with my old friend and wool magnate Prudence Prendergast, spinster of this parish, and scarlet wanton tart of every other. Just a joke, Pru.

There they go, chatting, and laughing, and pointing, and gambolling, and disappearing into the bushes, and ... and over there there's the village green, and ... Good Lord! I didn't know she had a pair that colour. What? Oh, yes, the village green.

Efforts are in hand to bring the village green up to date, although what date, no one's exactly sure. Boundless benefactor Lord Nose has donated a nice new winder for the sundial. The Crinkley Bottom Council's promised to dismantle the gibbet – just as soon as the last poll tax payer's coughed up. And the gent's WC has undergone a major brightening-up operation: the trunk's been whitewashed and a few of the top branches lopped off. It's nice to have a splash of natural greenery in the village.

Despite all this heady modernization, the village green remains the place where the old Crinkleyshire County Fair stands, usually when the owner's feeling reclusive, or in need of a hefty tax loss. Here, too, are enacted Crinkley Bottom's many ancient ceremonies, such as Standing Still While the Maypole Revolves Around You, and Crowning the Queen of the May – a custom which, with traditional Crinkley Bottom efficiency, occurs around the end of October.

Village sports flourish here, as well: football, croquet, rugby, tennis – you can never tell which, the way Crinkley Bottomers play them. And in the gnat-frolicking near distance, even as

Rush hour

we speak, groundsman Bert Liberace is preparing a cricket pitch with the roller. Hope he's remembered to clean the paint off it this time.

As the village green recedes in the rear-view mirror, we approach what is becoming by far the most familiar part of Crinkley Bottom – the village idiot. He's just on his way into the tobacconist's to ask why they've got his reflection in their shop window. It's appropriate because, turning right into Snogging Bint Lane – look out, old chap! You're wobbling all over the road. I wouldn't mind, but he's not even on a bicycle. Where was I? Oh, yes: turning into Snogging Bint Lane. Snogging Bint Lane is the area where Crinkley Bottom's retail traders chose to set up shop. Lucky, really, because this is where villagers come to buy things.

Look – I mean, don't look! I really shouldn't be bringing you down here. Snogging Bint Lane has a bit of a reputation locally, and you tend to see sights here you'd normally only see with subtitles on BBC 2. Time was when Crinkley Bottom policemen only let people down here after the nine o'clock watershed, and many's the early-morning postman who's had to be rushed to hospital with a dislocated eyeball. Still, if you avert your eyes – and try not to drool over the upholstery too much! I only had it cleaned after the last Coronation – we should be OK.

There, made it. Tenderpart Court. No, get off! I mean, we're in Tenderpart Court. It's a sort of eight-sided circular square. The far end, which is like the near end but closer, is blocked off by a line of six three-foot-high, grey bollard-like things. Villagers acclaimed their installation as a unique Council contribution to village traffic regulation – until they realized it was just where Terry Nutter had been leaving his chewing gum.

Along the top there's a huddle of shops: the health food store, closed owing to illness; the family butcher, closed when butchering families fell into disfavour here, last March; the wine shop, closed by the local Noise Abatement Society; Dianne Frizzett's Lunatic Fringe hair salon, closed because of a very small thing – well, a nest of very small things, actually; the greengrocer's, where the assistants simply can't do enough for you, so they usually don't bother.

Around the corner from them stand three somewhat more successful traders: the shrewd village eye doctor, with a slightly blurred 'Optician' sign over his door; the antiques shop, where locals come to update their possessions; and the Crinkley Bottom Bank, busy again today. They must have another sale on.

Further down, we've got the Pea Shoppe, behind that bundle of old rags and boulders. Oh no, sorry, that's Mrs Bulstrode. Next, there's Prudence Prendergast's Wool Shop, rumoured to have been in Crinkley Bottom since before sheep were invented – a bit like Pru herself. Joking, Pru! What with all the planks and scaffolding, the old Wool Shop's not looking its best at the moment: archaeologists are excavating the site of an ancient Roman settlement found above Pru's bedroom.

Hang on while I swing around this mini-roundabout – get out of it! – Twerp – where Monica Zoff is baffling the village idiot with common sense. Cor, I've not seen him for a while! People are putting up umbrellas now, which means it's either coming on to rain, or the window cleaner's dandruff's still not cleared up. Either way, it's good news for trade in the Crinkley Café, on your left now, hiding behind the statue of famous village explorer Terry Pindun-Dee.

You'll find plenty of local life in the

The village idiot

Crinkley Café, most of it in their pies. Not for nothing is this known as the place that put the uck in cookery, the eurgh in hors d'oeuvre, and the newt in nutriment. That said, the prices aren't unreasonable, and there's always plenty of food on the menu – the tablecloth, the carpet and the walls. The Crinkley Café is one of Crinkley Bottom's medium-class emporiums, which is good going in a village where most places need to be knocked down and completely rebuilt to be considered for slum clearance. As such, I think we'll pull over and have a closer look at it.

The first thing that grabs the eye is the mullioned bay window: it's double glazed – with glass and chip fat, and through it you can spy the local diners catching up on last Wednesday's breakfast. Pass me a tissue, would you?

Just inside the door, a chap eating bumpkin pie has complained to a waitress about the greasy lumps, so she's gone to find him a table away from the Nutter family. The Nutters themselves have brought six straws, and chosen soup of the day. From the look of it, I'd say the day in question was 8 March 1912.

Left of the Nutters, the VIP guest – he's the one with the chair – is Chippy Descartes the existential carpenter. He's dining with Chubby Attenborough in his 'Proud to be Humble' T-shirt; Lefty Hopalong Scarface Jameson, who's having one of those lives; and Rita Slaghips, the sumo golfer, who saves the best until last by eating her food backwards.

Over by the stomach pump trolley, we've got Larry Garry Harry Barry-Parry, who can't hear the letter C; and with him, nocturnal sunbather and part-time workaholic Jaws Bush. Well! I'm surprised to see him in the Crinkley Café. His cousin once grew a beard waiting to be served in here. The waiters apologized, but she was furious.

At the next table, spoon addict Donna Van Jason peers down at her steak, deciding whether to eat it or release it back into Muckflirter's Meadow. Alongside her, Kylie Firker, such a bad actress they named a wood after her, is ordering the Crinkley Café's most popular three-course meal – two puddings and a taster.

Course I'd take you in for a bite with them, only I seem to have forgotten my wallet. Not that there's more than the odd copper in it. And, talking of odd coppers, here comes Crinkley Bottom's own: Detective Constable Hugh Dunnett, with that bastion of motoring rectitude Priscilla the Hun, Traffic Warden from Hell.

How reassuring to see them out, patrolling these mean streets, hunting down fiendish crooks, heinous wrongdoers, and – oh, they're clomping over. Must want to thank me for my donation to the Crinkley Bottom Policemen's Fund. A sticking plaster always comes in handy, doesn't it? I'll just roll down the window, before they break it; s'cuse me a second.

Afternoon! Yes, yes, it's mine ... Edmonds ... Noel ... Noel St-John, Brad, Rocky, Finetime, Idi, Chuck Edmonds ... Charging me? What wi—? ... Reckless driving! ... Parking in a restricted zone! Me? ... What do you mean, fixed penalty? I've never played football in my life ... All right, hang on.

Er, look, would you mind awfully if we postpone this tour? Only I need to call my solicitor. No, I'm not defending the charge: I just want to ask if he'll lend me a tenner. Oh, nearly forgot. One last thing before I go – you haven't got ten pee for the phone, have you ...?

2. Turning Crinkley

To be a Cockney you have to be born within the sound of Bow Bells; to be a Glaswegian you have to be born between pub opening hours; and to be a Mancunian you have to be born with flippers. In Crinkley Bottom, things aren't as simple as that. They never are. Being a Crinkley Bottomer is less to do with your natal provenance, and more to do with your state of mind – although, considering the state of most Crinkley Bottomers' minds, it's hard to know how they came to be born at all. Or why.

Nor is it even necessary to start life as a Crinkley Bottomer. Villagership is a bit like a Spanish air-traffic controller; it strikes any time, any day, anywhere. And before you know it, you're being featured on the front page of the *Crinkley Bottom Observer* and having bad jokes made up about you by me on Saturday night.

So, what are the signs to beware of? What antiquated characteristics betray the true Crinkley Bottomer? How do you tell whether you're daft, dundering and decrepit enough to qualify for villagership? Hold on – why am I asking you? The following list, compiled after years of painstaking research by a top Crinkley Bottom nosey parker, provides you with all the symptoms to look out for, in frank and gruesome detail. (Readers of a nervous disposition should close their eyes now, and reopen them when they reach the end of the book.)

PARTIAL BOTTOMNESS
(See a doctor)

Being able to remember what happened to you on Saturday night.

Suspecting thermal underwear may not be such a bad idea after all.

Going to plug in the radio, and finding it's already on.

Yellow toenails.

Leaving the lights off and your socks on at bedtime.

Having one foot in the grave, and the other in a bowl of embrocation.

SERIOUS BOTTOMNESS
(See a vet)

Thinking that slipping into something more comfortable means putting your slippers on.

Discovering your waist to inside-leg ratio sounds more like the betting on a Grand National outsider.

The neighbours complaining about the noise when you finally peel your vest off.

Noticing that the only double-glazing salesmen to knock on your door are looking for somewhere to hide from the bull.

Having more material in your swimsuit than in your beach towel.

Finding the only thing that's long and hard in the morning

is getting out of bed.

Worrying that the nice mottled brown pattern on your pullover is really just the side-effects of a passing muckspreader.

ACUTE BOTTOMNESS
(See a circus proprietor)
Holding a passionate belief that 70 degrees Fahrenheit isn't what it used to be.

Becoming better acquainted with the patterns on the bathroom floor.

Thinking it's getting late at ten past nine.

Not being able to remember your first sweetheart's telephone number.

Discovering the police may be on your side after all.

Being asked the way to the garden centre with confidence.

Hoofprints inside your wellingtons

MEGA BOTTOMNESS
(See a taxidermist)
Losing interest in the library books on the bottom shelf.

Hunting everywhere for your glasses only to remember you don't wear glasses.

Coming to terms with the fact that the hair on your husband's collar is probably his own.

Suffering from a constant nagging suspicion that you're not being watched.

Deciding 20p pieces aren't worth bending down for any more.

Planning detours around your bedroom to avoid the full-length mirror.

Discovering that your idea of variety is using a different finger to change TV channels.

RAMPANT BOTTOMNESS
(See a miracle worker)
Wobbly elbow flesh.

Paying 50p to get in to see your local football team – and £10.50 to get out.

Talking to yourself and finding you're not listening any more.

Never going to the loo without something to read.

Realizing the only songs you can sing along with are on Radio 2.

Suspecting it would be easier to buy new shoes than to cut your toenails.

Admitting that the only part of your body that's still hard and stiff is your back.

Only knowing what day it is by the number of tablets left in the bottle.

3. The History

Professor Dosie-Pratt, lecturer in Intrinsically Boring Studies at Crinkleyshire University, charts the history of Crinkley Bottom from its primitive humble beginnings to its primitive humble present.

2,000,000,000 BC: Crinkley Bottom Man leaves primordial soup; orders chips instead.

2,000,000 BC: The Ice Age. Epidemic of heat rash in Crinkley Bottom.

500,000 BC: Crinkley Bottom Man discovers fire. 380 village huts burn down when he takes it to show his friends.

400,000 BC: Early man begins to use tools. First thumb split open in Crinkley Bottom.

A fool in action

35,000 BC: Neanderthal Man dies out. Too clever by half, say Crinkley Bottomers.

5,000 BC: Britain becomes separated from mainland Europe. Europeans try to get swimming lessons banned in Crinkley Bottom.

1,600 BC: Stonehenge unveiled. Bulstrode family corset builder sues for breach of copyright.

1,180 BC: Walls of Jericho collapse. Crinkley Bottom launches bid to buy their remaining stocks of ice-cream.

54: Romans in Crinkley Bottom build first road. It's a by-pass.

526: Discovery of the kiss: short-sighted couple in the Crinkley Tavern accidentally eat the same piece of spaghetti from different ends.

526: Crinkley Bottomers enjoy 526 so much, they have another one.

1066: Halley's Comet passes over Crinkley Bottom. Villagers assume the West Indies have started batting at Lord's.

1381: Peasants revolt under Wat Tyler. Crinkley Bottomers send him a cushion.

1397: Battle of Crinclium. Six-day conflict fought between Rupert Duke of Crinkleyshire and

16

invading French forces over control of Crinkley Bottom. Rupert wins and makes the French have it.

1427: No minke whales spotted in Crinkley Bottom all year. Fears grow.

1453: Crinkley Bottom Geographical Expedition sails off the end of the world.

1457: Crinkley Bottom participates in the Wars of the Roses. Villagers gather in Muckflirter's Meadow and throw chocolates at one another.

1512: Michelangelo paints the ceiling of the Sistine Chapel. Crinkley Bottom Council ask if he'll come and slap a couple of coats of emulsion on the village hall roof.

1539: Henry VIII spends a week in Crinkley Bottom: one day sightseeing; six wedged in the main street.

1589: Sir Walter Raleigh returns from four-year expedition to America, with a potato. Crinkley Bottomers advise him to go back to making bicycles.

1594: William Shakespeare visits Crinkley Bottom. Villagers so honoured, they offer to stage one of his concerts.

1605: The Great Crinkley Bottom Banana Fright. 362 villagers frightened by bananas.

9091: Crinkley Bottomers hang their calendars upside-down.

1637: Descartes makes famous philosophical statement: I think, therefore, I am. Crinkley Bottomers realize they've been imagining themselves.

1641: Crinkley Bottom mathematicians celebrate the golden anniversary of 1621.

1642: The English Civil War, in which one half of England becomes locked in a bloody battle with the other half. Crinkley Bottomers don kilts and start talking with a Welsh accent.

The Great Plague – not so great if you happen to catch it

1665: The Great Plague strikes Crinkley Bottom. The local doctor advises alarmed villagers to calm their nerves by stroking some small furry animal – like a rat.

1666: The Great Fire of Crinkley Bottom. Villagers throughout the county hasten to the scene with blankets, sheets, spare clothes, towels – anything, in fact, to fan the flames.

1675: Wren designs St Paul's Cathedral. Crinkley Bottomers try to work out how it held the pencil in its beak.

1678: Survey on living in Crinkley Bottom reveals the first ninety years are the worst.

1700: Crinkley Bottom's measles epidemic ends when the local doctor realizes he's splashed red paint on his spectacles.

1743: Notorious highwayman Half-Peck Edmonds's mini-reign of terror in Crinkley Bottom comes to an end when a lynch mob string him up from the nearest doorknob.

1720: A Crinkley Bottomer wins the World Giant Snowman Competition when he inserts two lumps of coal, a carrot and a pipe into the side of Mount Everest.

1787: Crinkley Bottom launderette regular Tubs Wogan circumnavigates the globe; still can't find his other sock.

1806: Crinkley Bottom's Second Arithmetic Teachers' Strike.

1808: Crinkley Bottom's First Arithmetic Teachers' Strike.

1811: The Great Crinkley Bottom Crimping Scissors Crisis. Crimping scissors in crisis throughout Crinkley Bottom.

1814: George Stephenson discovers it's possible to move inert objects by steam. Crinkley Bottom women immediately try holding a boiling kettle under their husbands.

1815: After escaping from Elba, Napoleon is exiled to St Helena, and warned – next time it's Crinkley Bottom!

1851: The Great Exhibition. Villagers flock to Hyde Park with their fireplaces.

1860: Charles Darwin visits Crinkley Bottom; looks puzzled.

1864: Formation of Crinkley Bottom Wonderers. When it is pointed out that football clubs don't have twenty players, Wonderers change their formation to 442.

1869: A Crinkley Bottomer wins the World Hide and Seek Championships. He hides in the Bermuda Triangle.

1870–71: Franco-Prussian War. Crinkley Bottom supports Spain.

1883: Crinkley Bottom Birth Strike ends when pregnant village women find they're unable to withdraw their labour.

1895: Crinkley Bottomer invents early radio. Idea scrapped when it's pointed out that most villagers don't get up until after eleven a.m.

1910: Government committee devises method of doubling Britain's average IQ. They propose giving Crinkley Bottom independence.

1911: Seven-and-a-half-year-old Crinkley Bottom boy becomes the first person to reach the South Pole. His mother says she only sent him out for a Penguin.

1912: *Titanic* sinks on maiden voyage. Crinkley Bottom villagers launch boat to rescue the iceberg.

1915: Crinkley Bottom's wartime evacuation plans revised. Government finds it quicker to leave the people and move the village.

1920: Mrs Bulstrode's birth registers 6.3 on the Richter Scale.

1923: Crinkley Bottom motor factory opens. Villagers cheer as the first car is pushed off the production line. Hereafter, owners of Crinkley Bottom motor vehicles become known by a special name. They're called pedestrians.

1924: Year goes unrecorded. Entire village sleeps in.

1925: Crinkley Bottom Wonderers reach Wembley for FA Cup Final. They leave the coach and take their seats in Block F, Row G.

1926: The General Strike. In Crinkley Bottom, all high-ranking army officers stop work.

1928: First Mickey Mouse cartoon goes on release. 600 Crinkley Bottomers sue for libel.

1936: Crinkley Bottom to Dangley End Road opens. 3,487 Dangley Enders move.

1946: A Crinkley Bottomer becomes the first man to reach the summit of Everest. He falls out of a plane.

1948: The Crinkley Bottom Beer Crisis. Liszt and Newt down to last 3,000 gallons.

1949: Building begins on the first houses in Crinkley Bottom to incorporate electric light and mains drainage. (Should be finished any day now.)

1950: First meal ordered in Crinkley Café.

1952: First meal served in Crinkley Café.

1954: Roger Bannister achieves first sub-four-minute mile. Sceptical Crinkley Bottomers ask, Did he have the periscope up or down?

1955: Crinkley Bottom becomes a smokeless zone. Villagers celebrate with a bonfire.

1956: Crinkley Café waitress locates first tip from Noel Edmonds; uses it to pay Noel for loan of his magnifying glass.

1958: The Beast of Tiddler's Lake is spotted. Liszt and Newt regulars warned to be more careful where they spend a penny.

1959: Electric chair demonstrated. Crinkley Bottom traffic warden Priscilla the Hun places an order for an electric village bench.

1960: The Great Crinkley Bottom Coathanger Shortage. Disaster narrowly averted.

1963: The Great Train Robbery. Crinkley Bottomers on the lookout for a man trying to sell them a train.

1964: Plan to twin Crinkley Bottom with cartoon prehistoric village Bedrock dropped when it's described as demeaning, odious, insulting, humiliating and distasteful. Crinkley Bottomers don't like the sound of it much, either.

1966: England make footballing history and beat West Germany to win the World Cup. Crinkley Bottomers tuned to the film on BBC 2.

1969: Man's first lunar landing. Villagers gather beneath the moon, and wave.

1970: Crinkley Bottom suffragettes' march for universal suffrage sets out. Spelling on placards right at last!

1972: First manned expedition to the top of Terry Nutter's dog.

1974: Lord Lucan disappears. Last seen asking a Crinkley Bottom villager for directions.

1977: Servants end wages strike at the Great House when Noel finally agrees to pay them some.

1988: Crinkley Bottom Outing Society returns from trip to Greece. Members complain it's nothing like the film.

1990: Rumours of financial irregularities in Mirror Group Newspapers' pension fund. Crinkley Bottomers withdraw their money, and invest it in the Bank of Credit and Commerce International.

1991: Introduction of the Poll Tax sparks angry riots in Crinkley Bottom. Villagers say it's just not high enough.

1993: The Official Guide to Crinkley Bottom is published. Half the villagers vow never to speak to Noel Edmonds again. Noel immediately begins work on the sequel.

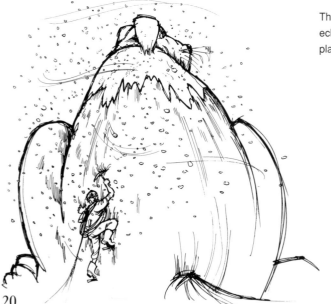

The dog that eclipsed a planet

4. Fashion

Let's get one thing straight right away. There is no truth whatsoever in the rumour that woad and loincoths are back in fashion in Crinkley Bottom. They've never been out.

This does not mean that village fashions are in any way outmoded. Crinkley Bottomers don't know the meaning of the word. Or any other two-syllable word, for that matter. Flouncy gowns, black-lace garters, and frilly knickers are commonly seen in the village. Admittedly, the men wearing them get some funny looks. But since the startling discovery of the Button here last year and with many villagers now mastering the art of changing their clothes occasionally, the Crinkley Bottom fashion industry has made great strides – and some pretty nifty jackets to match.

The village's exclusive clothing emporia The Shoe Must Go On (the shop that puts the boot into boutique), Thread Sales (a division of the Dud Clobber chain), and Corsets in Fashion (the store that takes the cost out of costumes) are inundated with up to twenty customers each year, eagerly rooting out the latest village couture – to wit:

Frock for a party: a party of sixteen to be exact

ARROW-PROOF VEST - £60
STOAT TWEAKER'S BOILER SUIT - £40
FERRET-PROOF UNDERPANTS - £15
STILETTO-HEELED WELLINGTONS - £12
   (£16 for 3)
HIS 'N' HERS VETERINARY GAUNTLETS - £12
POACHER'S JACKET (with secret trout pocket) - £35

PEASANT-HIDE MONEY BELT
   (holds up to 23 salt sacks) - £14
GENUINE NOEL EDMONDS CARDIGAN
   - £250, or £35 per cwt
TWO-TONE T-SHIRTS (green only) - £7.50
DUAL-PURPOSE MATERNITY DRESS
   (including tent pegs) - £35
HEAVY-DUTY BLOOMERS
   (6 years' parts and service warranty) - £20
REVERSIBLE WOOLLY HAT
   (with instructions) - £8
STRAP-ON CEREMONIAL SWORD AND
MATCHING PLASTERS - £50
PRU PRENDERGAST'S HAND-KNITTED
NIGHTGOWN (padlocks not included) - £22
UTILITY KNICKERBOCKERS
   (Bagpipe pocket!) - £14

Inflatable underpants: withdrawn after they were found to give Crinkley Bottom men a headache

ARMOUR-PLATED UNDERWEAR
  (for unavoidable visits to the Great House) - £30
NON-STICK CODPIECE (with packing or free loan of
  bicycle pump) - £8.50
MULTI-PURPOSE GIRDLE/SHEEP PEN - £32
BEST CLOGS (choice of laces) - £12
CRINKLEYSHIRE CAMOUFLAGE JACKET (pub-
  wallpaper or Friesian-cow design) - £42
OAPs' SPECIAL: FISHNET VEST AND HALTER-
NECK TROUSERS - £19.99
PLASTIC MAC (with plimsolls and plan of Firker's
  Wood) - £12
VILLAGE DANCE BALLGOWN (with rope and
  chandelier attachment) – £69.90
EX-NOEL EDMONDS BREECHES (made from the
  skin of a single hamster) - FREE

With such sumptuous clothing on offer, it's little wonder that a certain royal personage was observed in Crinkley Bottom last year, purchasing garments to keep her loved ones warm in the winter. Naturally, she didn't go away empty-handed, and word has it the corgis' baskets have never been so snug.

The fashion industry in Crinkley Bottom is not limited to mere vending, however. Many's the local farmer who's cranked up his tractor and towed his wife's unmentionables to Corsets for riveting and a quick rub-down with sandpaper before the village dance.

One's mind also recalls Baggy Schofield, whose interlaced wind socks – or trousers as he called them – bettered his inside-leg measurement by twenty-nine feet. Thread Sales staff still talk of the day he dropped in, from 15,000 feet, to get them shortened. What a turn up that was!

Yes, Crinkley Bottom fashion is bursting out all over – and the industry's bracing itself for a belting future. An annual Best Dressed Man competition has been introduced (this year's hot favourite is Mr Long of the Naturist Society); and the order obtained recently from Crinkley Bottom's haulage company – Artic Roles – is already proving a great success. Even as I speak, a lorry driver's pulled up outside Corsets, using one of their new spring frocks to rope up his load.

Satin ensemble: so-called because it looks as though it's been sat in for weeks

22

5. Dateline Crinkley Bottom

With the *Crinkley Bottom Observer*, *Herald*, *Bungle*, and *Sunday Fibber* selling like rotten fruit at Toepoker Park since the local toilet paper mill folded, freelance journalist Maurice Chinking-Jacket reveals how you too can become a writer for Crinkley Bottom's local papers.

Hold it right there. I said, Freeze! Good. Now, let go of the page. That's right; drop it nice and gently, keep your eyes on the words, don't get any silly ideas about skipping on to the next bit until you reach the end of this, OK?

See, you don't change your mind half-way through an appendectomy – tell the surgeon, sorry, but if it's all the same to him, you'd prefer a liver transplant instead. So you don't break off half a dozen sentences into a literary gem, and flick over for a butcher's at the next cartoon, right? Right.

What the average bumpkin in the field fails to appreciate is the sheer guts that go into this er, writing stuff. Some Crinkley Bottom hacks suffer months of mental turmoil before they can start – and even when they've actually found a pen, like as not the tip's dried up, or they've forgotten what they were going to write about in the first place.

But don't run away with the idea that all you need is a reliable memory and a decent pen. It may be true. But our lives would be hell if the Inland Revenue ever found out. So if you've ever wondered what it takes to be a Crinkley Bottom hack, here's a guide to the absolutely essential things you'll need. Wink, wink.

A UNIFORM

These days, it's not enough merely to be a local paper hack: you've got to be seen to be a local paper hack. And you can't do this by slobbing round the house in pyjama bottoms and a trawler-net vest all week. You could be mistaken for a musician, or the Crinkley Bottom vicar, for goodness' sake.

Maurice Chinking-Jacket, aged 17 $\frac{1}{2}$

So you have to wear something distinctive – a garment which conveys an assured, calm outward sophistication, while at the same time suggesting a roiling sea of raw emotion within. In short, you've got to wear a cardigan. A woolly one, with big round buttons, and pockets you can bathe your elbows in. Dead cool.

Get this right, and the rest of the uniform's a piece of cake, or rather it's a pair of twelve-ply corduroy trousers, serious slippers, cravat, horn-rimmed specs, pipe, and ink stains – any colour you like, so long as it's blue.

Despite popular conception, though, a trailing reed warbler's-nest beard is purely an optional component of the hack's uniform. But sporting one unquestionably singles you out as a distinctive member of the literary establishment. Particularly if you're a woman.

A PSEUDONYM

Pseudonyms are just about the only part of a manuscript that Crinkley Bottom hacks bother to spell right, so they really go to village on them. Plausibility flies out of the window. Vanity creeps in. Impossible initials appear, sudden hyphens wriggle between the words like teenaged moped-riders in a traffic jam. To be blunt: if you want to join the Crinkley Bottom literati, noms de plume like Alf Balls, Madge Frost and Dennis Pugh simply aren't exotic enough any more. Even Marmoset Willoughby-Yaksnout's a bit ordinary for the contemporary pen-handler. And as for Jeffrey Archer ...

No. The Crinkley Bottom hack needs a pseudonym that will stick in the villagers' minds ... memories and throats: something awesome, something momentous, something with more letters than British Rail's complaints department – something, in fact, like O. Zachary Maximus Phelan-Fennislow, Marcantonio F.-X. Hackenbacker Junior, or Glenys Goewin de Gwnifor Owen-Money, to name but ten. A threat to the world's printing ink supply they may be; but such sobriquets provide hacks with that essential air of mystery and menace, humour and romance. More importantly, when you're up to your neck in stationery bills, and the next commission seems about as imminent as Crinkley Bottom Wonderers winning the European Cup, they throw the taxman off your scent a treat.

A LOT OF PAPER

It takes a special kind of skill to sit behind a typewriter all day and produce a flawlessly blank sheet of paper. Too much skill for most hacks. They insist on besmirching the page with what can almost be described as words – no less than four, no more than eight – before screwing it up, hurling it two feet to the left of a waste-paper basket, and going off in search of biscuits.

On a good day, a Crinkley Bottom hack should aim to screw up anything between sixty and ninety sheets per minute. This is a sign that the hack is being creative – he's creating a minor ecological crisis in the world's rain forests.

A GARDEN SHED

You'll need one of these to store all those touchingly personal rejection slips in when you become a full-time Crinkley Bottom hack. A modest twelve-by-twelve structure should be adequate to house your first million; you can always build an extension on if your career enters a second week.

The Crinkley Bottom hack's workshop in its natural state – empty

AN ABHORRENCE OF CLICHÉS

Crinkley Bottom hacks should avoid clichés like the plague.

A PARANOIA

Crinkley Bottomers have strange ideas about paranoias; they think they're some kind of voracious South American river-fish. They're not. Honestly. But though they don't have steel jaws and lethal appetites, make no mistake – paranoias are still out to get you in the end – and most other parts of your body.

To be awfully clever, a paranoia is a fixed mental delusion frequently characterized by an irrational belief that one is the object of personal persecution. And if you're ever going to make it as a hack on the Crinkley Bottom press, you're going to need lots of them: a delusion that you're not being paid enough; a delusion that someone's being employed full-time to hide your pen; a delusion that people don't really believe you're the reincarnation of William Shakespeare; a delusion that the Post Office has set up a special department to divert all your incoming mail to an adobe hut in Peru; and, above all, a delusion that someone is going to ridiculous lengths to copy your work.

While other paranoias may be adopted or rejected according to taste, or lack of it, this last is a must for all hacks. Sounds boring? Don't kid yourself; this is probably the finest excuse for virulently anti-social behaviour since Monday mornings were invented.

Sufferers can kick the cat into orbit with complete impunity, take potshots at paperboys who eavesdrop at the front door pretending to read your *Sunday Fibber*, lock the wife in the loft on the grounds that she might open her mouth for three seconds down the Crinkley Bottom Co-op and blow the ideas for your next ninety-five articles.

Some hacks achieve such enviable degrees of paranoia, they erect electric fences round their typewriters and have burglar alarms fitted in their heads. Others have been known to wrap their entire worldly goods in a spotted handkerchief, and spend the rest of their lives hunched over notebooks at the bottom of a disused plutonium-239 mine in the Australian outback. All very admirable. Although if you're really serious about isolating yourself from civilization, why not just pack a bag and move to Upper Bottom?

A SENSE OF PROPORTION

There's an old saying: writing is 10 per cent inspiration, 90 per cent perspiration. Nonsense. The only time a Crinkley Bottom hack sweats is when the annual buff envelope from HM's Collector of Blood evades the Post Office's diversion, and drops on his doormat. A far more realistic assessment of the ingredients of our art would be 3 per cent inspiration, 2 per cent perspiration, 95 per cent inebriation. Before attempting to achieve this indelicate balance, new writers should see their Crinkley Bottom editors. It always pays to watch an expert.

AN EDITOR

Strange word, editor: six letters, three syllables, and you pronounce it God. Hacks need an editor like diners at Crinkley Bottom's Indian restaurant need a personal exclusion zone. And for much the same reason. But editors aren't just an outlet; they're also highly experienced providers of varied and valued input. Like money. And money. So which Crinkley Bottom newspaper editor should you choose, and where do you find him? Hold on!

One question at a time! Mention money, and you leus all cents of control and just go to pesos.

Firstly, selection. Here, it's wise to remember that editors fall into two traps: those who spend 50 per cent of their lives 100 per cent drunk; and those who spend 100 per cent of their lives 50 per cent drunk. There are also sub-categories who spend 75 per cent of their lives 25 per cent drunk, and 25 per cent of their lives 75 per cent drunk. Some particularly bad cases spend

The Editor of the *Crinkley Bottom Observer*. 23 bottles to the minute

40 per cent of their lives wondering whether they're 30 per cent drunk or 30 per cent sober. And others are just too drunk, too often, to care.

But these petty distinctions need not concern you unduly. When choosing one of our village editors, just ask yourself one question: will there be a point in the month when the old soak's both drunk enough to sign you a cheque, and sober enough not to post it down his secretary's blouse? If the answer's no, look elsewhere. If it's yes, call me immediately.

Next question: trying to find your Crinkley Bottom editor. Here, you're in good company. Lots of people are trying to find Crinkley Bottom editors – Scotland Yard, HP companies, Crinkley Bottom editors' wives, Crinkleyshire court bailiffs, local au pair girls'

brothers. Assuming you can shuffle your way to the front of this pack, it's advisable to begin your hunt systematically. First, find out where he works: that twilit world of tooth-scarred typewriters and unread manuscript mountains. Mark it prominently on your Crinkley Bottom map, and make a point never to go within fifty yards of it – it's the last place he'll be.

Having eliminated the impossible, whatever remains – however obvious – must be the solution. So check your watch. If it's round with numbers on the outside, he'll be in the Liszt and Newt. If it's not round with numbers on the outside, he'll be in the Liszt and Newt as well. If you can't afford a watch, don't look any further; you're probably a Crinkley Bottom hack already.

6. Weather View

You rarely hear the weather mentioned in Crinkley Bottom, and a belief has grown up that this is because the village is so boring, it doesn't have any. This is simply not true. The real reason the weather's not mentioned in Crinkley Bottom is that locals find it just too exciting to talk about.

Not wishing, therefore, to precipitate an epidemic of hyperventilation by asking the villagers about their wet fronts and fog pockets, I gave a top BBC weather man two fir cones and a moist finger, and told him to explain the local climate for us. Well, it seemed like a good idea at the time.

Ah! there I am. Now, the Crinkley Bottom climate. What is it? Where does it come from? What's it got against Terry Nutter's car? Why can't Flossie Rantzen pronounce it? And why does it turn the village idiot's boil six different colours, all of them yellow? There is a short and simple answer to all these questions, and I am rather proud to say I haven't the foggiest idea what it is. But that's never stopped a BBC weatherman before, so here we go and, so as not to confuse you, I'll start at the beginning with the first bit first.

TEMPERATURE: How hot it is in Crinkley Bottom depends on the temperature; and, as you can see from the meterolo– metoreol– meteorel–climatic graph, in winter, it's squiggly, and in summer it's sort of humpy. In real money, this means that if you like humpy temperatures, you should visit Crinkley Bottom in the summer, and if you don't, you er, shouldn't.

FOG: An attempt to discover how big a problem fog is in Crinkley Bottom was abandoned recently when villagers decided it was too foggy to tell.

RAIN: It's said that rain rarely falls in Crinkley Bottom because there's nowhere for it to go. That's just a little joke for intending visitors, because they're going to need something to make them smile when they get here. But back to rain. This is where the climatic graph really comes into its own, showing us that Crinkley Bottom's driest period is in the months when there's least rainfall, and its wettest is in the cricket season. Incidentally, if, after studying the graph, you're still unsure about the amount of rain Crinkley Bottom receives, go outside, find a villager, and squeeze him.

The Crinkley Bottom monsoon of 1963 failed to put village batsmen off their stroke – they all got a duck

FROST: Frost occurs in Crinkley Bottom under only two specific circumstances: down in the village when the temperature falls below zero; and up around the Great House when somebody asks for a rise.

SNOW: There are two things you can say for definite about snow in Crinkley Bottom: one, it happens in winter; and two (and this is really spooky), it always coincides with falls of cold white fluffy stuff. As for predicting when to expect snow, this is never easy, but as a general rule look out for it when the weather forecasters tell you it's going to be warm and dry.

CLOUD COVER: Contrary to popular belief, you can get cloud cover in Crinkley Bottom. The Crinkley Bottom Insurance Company provides cover for all kinds of clouds at very reasonable rates.

HAIL: The hail season causes havoc in the quaint little village of Crinkley Bottom – half a dozen hailstones, and the main street can be blocked for weeks. Happily, real hailstorms only affect Crinkley Bottom in winter. Those big chunks of ice which rain down on the village at other times of the year are just the fridge being cleaned out up at the Great House.

WIND: Globally, wind is the movement of air from an atmospherically hot region, such as the Azores, to a cold one, such as Northern Europe. The same principle applies in Crinkley Bottom, though on a much smaller scale – so small in fact that if the village baker Dick O'Crumbs opens his oven to take out a dozen loaves in south-west Crinkley Bottom while Mrs Bulstrode is removing a packet of petits pois from the Pea Shoppe fridge in the north-east of the village, the prevailing local air movements will be south-westerlies. Thus, Crinkley Bottom villagers are able to influence their wind by buying either bread or peas. Which comes as a bit of a shock to those of us who thought we could influence it by buying either beans or charcoal biscuits.

GALES: Structural damage owing to the weather can never be ruled out in Crinkley Bottom. Unless you're Michael Fish. But I can safely say that you'll only get gales in the village when the wind exceeds 35 mph.

By now, you'll be asking yourself, Is anything certain about the Crinkley Bottom weather? Well, in a word, yes. In another word, no. If that's not clear, let me add a word of my own. Maybe.

The little village is hit by a hailstorm

7. On the Box

People often ask me: what's that wobbly long pole-like thing protruding above the Great House on Crinkley Bottom's skyline? I tell them to go away and stop bothering me when I'm in the bath.

Sometimes, however, these are not personal comments at all, but references to the aerial of Crinkley Bottom's cable television station, cleverly known as Crinkley Bottom Cable.

There exists an ingrained and rather violent antipathy towards this new-fangled cable television service in Crinkley Bottom, predominantly among those villagers who subscribe to it.

It's true that Crinkley Bottom Cable's programming has met with one or two slight catastrophes: the chat show hosted by the Abbot of Crinkley Bottom's Trappist monastery, for instance. And calling coverage of ninety-three-year-old Gladys Dangley's funeral a live broadcast probably wasn't such a good idea, either. And what can you say about allowing Terry Nutter and his German Shepherd/baby Brontosaurus cross to compete in a televised local *One Man and His Dog* contest that wasn't said a dozen times by the coroner at the inquest?

But lately, Crinkley Bottom Cable has been trying to improve its service. To show it is a caring station, the results of all recorded Crinkley Bottom Wonderers' matches are now broadcast well in advance so viewers won't have to watch them. Also, subtitles have been added to the coverage of local council debates for the hard of believing. And their recent bid to introduce Crinkleyshire's first twenty-four-hour sports channel would have been a great success, if only they'd been able to find enough sports that lasted twenty-four hours.

In its latest attempt to become more viewer-friendly, Crinkley Bottom Cable has put together a glossary of those obscure TV terms which flash across the screen and puzzle those viewers lucky enough to have turbo-charged eyes.

That glossary is reproduced here with Crinkley Bottom Cable's kind permission and a watertight guarantee that they will pick up the bill for any libel writs arising from its publication.

STAR: Theoretically, an exalted media personality of incalculable talent, ingenuity and charisma. Practically, anyone above the level of tea-lady.

SUPERSTAR: Anyone above the level of tea-lady who owns his own wig.

The CBTV hi-tech sound system is prepared for Crinkley Bottom's Gala Evening of Mime

NATIONAL CELEBRITY: Figure disliked by the whole nation.

NEWSREADER (MALE): Man with a wardrobe full of ties, shirts and jackets, and one pair of trousers.

NEWSREADER (FEMALE): Woman who brings you the latest hairstyles.

DIRECTOR: Member of a production team who tries to transform a simple concept into a major, glittering, big-budget epic.

PRODUCER: Member of a production team who tries to stop him.

TECHNICIAN: Expert skilled in the art of absenteeism.

SHOCK ABSORBER: Technical term for the CBTV Duty Officer.

REMOTE-CONTROL UNIT: Technical term for the CBTV Board Of Governors.

EXPENSES: Alcohol.

LUNCH HOUR: Time of recuperation in the middle of the day designed to give technicians a rest between tea-breaks.

TEA-BREAK: Like a lunch hour, only longer.

REHEARSALS: Period of preparation spent anticipating the start of a tea-break.

O.B.: Lucrative day out for a film crew, including five-star accommodation, petrol allowance, bonus payments, picnic hamper, free ice-creams and six blank cheques per man. Short for Over Budget.

It's tough at the top: CBTV's O.B. unit seek out material for their programme on agoraphobia.

PROGRAMME: Those long boring bits between the adverts.

SIT COM: Short, humorous programme, not intended to be taken seriously by viewers. The weather forecast is one of the better examples.

SOAP: Dramatic re-creation of ordinary, everyday life, comprising such ordinary, everyday incidents as murder, fraud, adultery, underworld crime, gaolbreaks, multi-million-pound take-overs, and UFO abduction. Ordinary, everyday viewers who watch too much are in grave danger of becoming addicted – to turning off.

CHAT SHOW: Confidential art-to-art conversation involving two superstars, six million eavesdroppers, and a new book.

NEWS: Full, frank reports of all the important events in Princess Diana's life.

PARTY POLITICAL BROADCAST: Nature's way of telling you to change channels.

SCHEDULING: Complex and highly skilled method of arranging for all your favourite programmes to be on different channels at the same time.

REPEAT: Programme which was watched by so few people the first time round, TV bosses think they can safely risk showing it again.

OLD FAVOURITE: Repeat.

FIRST SHOWN ON ... : Repeat.

ANOTHER OPPORTUNITY TO SEE: Repeat.

AND NOW ON BBC 2 ... : Repeat.

RETROSPECTIVE SEASON: Lots of repeats.

TRIBUTE: Repeated repeat.

CLASSIC: Repeated repeat which has been repeatedly repeated so often, the colour's begun to fade.

SOUNDTRACK: Specially commissioned musical score, designed to fill the dialogue gaps when broadcast on TV, and the producer's wallet when released on CD.

MICRO-MILLI-NANOSECOND: Period of time between the final line of a programme, and the continuity announcer's voice swooping in to tell you what's on next.

MINI-SERIES: Short serial whose final episode is broadcast on the evening you're always out. The prefix 'mini' is an acronym referring to the series' audience appeal and viewer profile, namely Minority Interest, Negligible Intelligence.

VIEWING FIGURES: Diversion indulged in by superstars on the beach at Cannes.

LICENCE FEE: Annual charge paid to the BBC which allows viewers to continue watching ITV throughout the coming year.

TAKE ONE!: Invitation uttered by a technician returning from the bar with a tray of expenses.

IN THE CAN: One of four methods of acquiring one's expenses, the others being: via the bottle, from the glass, and out of the bucket.

CHANNEL 4: The station viewers normally turn to when there's nothing on BBC 1, ITV or BBC 2. So-called because it normally takes them four minutes to realize there's nothing on this channel, either.

24-HOUR TV: 8-hour TV, 16-hour rubbish.

VINTAGE TV: Reminder of how awful black and white television used to be.

TV TIMES: Reminder of how awful modern television still is.

SATELLITE TV: Another opportunity to see a classic old favourite in a season of retrospective tributes. First shown on BBC 1, BBC 2, ITV, Channel 4, S4C ...

8. On the Road

Vital information for the Crinkleyshire motorist seeking to explore new villages, visit interesting people and criticize them.

CRINKLEY BOTTOM

Crinkley Bottom is by far the safest of all Crinkleyshire villages to drive in – provided you stay well clear of the roads. When motoring in Crinkley Bottom, never forget the local rule of the road: all Crinkley Bottomers drive on the right. And give way to the left. Sometimes.

NAFFAL-TO-SEA

Most local authorities impose limits on the length of time motorists may spend at the wheel. In Naffall, you can drive for just thirty-nine seconds. Any longer, and you crash off the pier into the Bristol Channel.

MONK'S BOTTOM

In summer, Monk's Bottom roads become terribly clogged. Traffic's partly responsible, but it's predominantly due to the locals' melted wellingtons sticking to the road surface. Motorists travelling to Monk's Bottom for seasonal work must expect to encounter big job losses, as the leaking WC still hasn't been sorted out.

DANGLEY END

Even cerebral movement in Dangley End tends to be slow. But progress is being made, and Dangley Council is confidently predicting the invention of the road any day now. Motorists wishing to avoid serious delays should postpone their journeys by about a century.

EDMONDS ISLAND

Edmonds Island is not a village; it's an inhabited microchip. As such, the road system is just a shade cramped. Well, let's be honest; the double-white lines overlap, the zebra crossings are monochrome, and the dual carriageways are stacked on top of one another. As a long-suffering British motorist, this should not inconvenience you unduly; just remember to fit an aqualung and waterwings before attempting a three-point turn.

MAD PRATT'S CROSS

Motorists in Mad Pratt's Cross must anticipate hold-ups. These may be prevented simply by running the highwayman down before he gets his pistols out.

NETHER SCRATCHING

Nether Scratching is not open to motorists all year round. In winter, the village becomes a surgery for claustrophobia aversion therapy; in summer, they whitewash the borders, and use it as a cricket pitch.

RUBBIT-UNDER-WATER

All approach roads to Rubbit-under-Water are still dangerously flooded. However, the local mafia have kindly offered to build a new flyover, and they're currently appealing for volunteers to mix with the cement.

COPPIT-UP-THE-JUNCTION

Motoring through Coppit-up-the-Junction is a pleasant, scenic and trouble-free experience. It's when you stop that you hit problems. Remain motionless anywhere in this village for more than thirty seconds, and they confiscate your car, nick your wallet and conscript your wife. Little wonder the place is becoming increasingly popular with second honeymooners.

THROTTLE ST EDMONDS

Motorists in Throttle St Edmonds should encounter very little traffic this year. The Government's banned everyone from the road until the whole village sobers up.

LITTLE BROWNING-ON-THE-HUMMOCK

The motorist in Little Browning will undoubtedly encounter plenty of jams at this time of year – and quite a wide choice of marmalades. But if they're anything like the recycled straw postcards that pass for bread in Little Browning, you're well advised to roll up your windows and take a packed lunch.

BOSKY WOOD-UNDER-THREAT

Intending visitors to Bosky Wood-under-Threat will be pleased to hear that the local fire brigade have now abandoned all attempts to clear remaining Second World War tanks from their roads. They've put little lights on the corners and called them Volvos.

Throttle St Edmonds: motorists and villagers are being held up

BUMPKIN'S END
There's a Bank Holiday in Bumpkin's End all this year.

GREAT BONKING-IN-THE-MEADOW
Great Bonking-in-the-Meadowers have something of a reputation for being idle and unambitious layabouts, and there's even a rumour that motorists there can forget road traffic regulations because they don't even have a road. This is untrue, inaccurate and extremely unfair. On average they have one about once every forty lay-bys.

MAGGOTY HOLE
The only problem with Maggoty Hole is how to find the place. At the moment, seasoned travellers should discover most Maggoty Holans at the bottom of a muddy cul-de-sac just off the B9763, 45 litres south-west of the Crinkleyshire Pop and Crisps Festival. Legend has it they're hiding from the Eurovision Song Contest.

PINKYTOWN
Motorists hoping to break through the red tape along Pinkytown's western border must expect those typical little local delays: you know – passport inspections, visa checks, luggage X-rays, body searches, intestine inspections, and brainwashing. But don't run away with the idea that the Pinkytonians don't want you to get into their country; quite the reverse – they don't want you to get out again. Play safe, and add about thirteen years to your journey time.

WEATHER ELLARWEE
As a safety precaution, you're advised to notify the Weather Ellarwee authorities forty-eight hours in advance of arrival. This gives them plenty of time to put the entire population into quarantine before your visit.

CRINKLETON
Motorists must expect slow progress in Crinkleton for quite some time yet. Their road is being repaired, and, word is, they might even have to take it back to the shop!

NICKEREDGE-ON-VUE
Nickeredge-on-Vue is undergoing extensive roadworks right now: they're turning it into the long awaited Crinkleton–Nether Scratching by-pass.

MOISTPATCH SPA
Sharp-eyed motorists in Crinkleyshire will notice that all travellers on the roads into Moistpatch Spa are manic depressives, psychopaths, nutters, cranks, or lunatics. There's a good reason for this: it's because no one in his right mind wants to go there.

GOBBIT-IN-THE-BOG
All roads in Gobbit are clear. They make them out of cling-film.

LITTLEWICK-ON-THE-RISE
There's just one thing standing in the way of Littlewick-on-the-Rise being the ideal motoring destination – the inhabitants. Sadly, no matter how hard you try, it's virtually impossible to travel through Littlewick without encountering the odd Littlewickian. And most Littlewickians are distinctly odd. But not quite as odd as their transport system.

Littlewickian crossroads, for instance, are only mildly annoyed; Littlewickian lollipop ladies melt in warm weather; the Littlewickian upper class have anglepoise street-lamps; posh Littlewickian zebra crossings come in three colours; and Littlewickian motorists are so anxious not to appear biased, they all drive in the middle of the road. Needless to say, Littlewick-bound hitchhikers should make an early start to avoid the traffic.

FONDLIT-BY-THE-RIDGE

To say that travel in Fondlit-by-the-Ridge is behind the times is like saying Fergie enjoys the odd day off. And we're not just talking a lot of cobblestones here; the place is positively primeval. Fondlit road-planning is done by volcano, and the local toffs impress their neighbours by parking a new native with a forked stick in the drive. For intending visitors, therefore, preparation for such appalling conditions and backward inhabitants is a must. And fortunately, this isn't hard to acquire. You can either take a degree in mid-Palaeolithic demography, or take a drive round mid-Wales.

Give or take a Stegosaurus, they amount to the same thing.

HACKDORF-BY-THE-COPSE

Motorists will find it easy to get about in Hackdorf-by-the-Copse. Simply by visiting one of the famous roadside cafés, you can get a bout of dysentery, dyspepsia, diarrhoea, salmonella poisoning, listeria, gastro-enteritis ...

MUCH PEEPING-IN-THE-DARQUE

Much Peeping-in-the-Darque, which was once to travelling what eunuchs are to procreation, is now really sharpening up its act transport-wise. Out have gone the peat-fired traction-engines; man-powered flight has been almost eliminated; most steam-trains now carry spare rubber bands; taxi-drivers are learning not to drag their knuckles along the ground; and the Much Peeping people are waving a fond farewell to their old hydrogen airships – at least, they are when the pilot hits a dark cloud, and decides to light the gas lamps.

Fondlit-by-the-Ridge: motorists might find it hard not to exceed the IQ limit

9. Warden Off the Evil Eye

Not all residents of Crinkley Bottom are bumptious, easy-going, cheery, quaint old halfwits. I'm not, for one. No, I'm not! And neither is the village traffic warden, Priscilla the Hun.

Priscilla is to Crinkley Bottom motorists what a veterinary gauntlet is to the local cows. You don't mess with Priscilla. She hates condescension. In fact, she's not particularly fond of any cooled gaseous vapour.

Get caught on one of her double-yellows, and by Jove! you'd better have a good reason, because the alternative is too hideous to spell out in a genteel work like this. Suffice it to say that it involves your own hand being forced into an intimately private place, and the extraction of actual m-m-m-money – without the aid of anaesthetic!

I think you get the picture. So you'll welcome the following list of excuses, all guaranteed to stop you breaking into a cold sweat or – more importantly – a £20 note, should you ever get caught double-parked by Crinkley Bottom's answer to Dirty Harry.

ALMOST PLAUSIBLE

Good Lord! I thought they put those yellow lines there to help you align your tyres.

I get agoraphobic in car parks.

There's a rumour the Queen's coming to pick up her groceries; I'm reserving a space for her.

I thought that by leaving my car on these lines, I could stop people parking here.

It's a Skoda; I was hoping someone would tow it away.

MILDLY UNBELIEVABLE

I keep getting these delusions that I'm a doctor on call.

There was a sudden heatwave; the paint melted; and my tyres got stuck.

Yes, I admit it! I'm a fixed-penalty-ophiliac.

The car's reversing at exactly the same speed as the Earth's forward rotational velocity; so it only looks as though it's stationary.

Typical, isn't it? You leave your car in a quiet country field, and when you come back twenty-five years years later, somebody's put a main street and a couple of yellow lines under it!

It's not parked; I'm trying to drive it by telekinesis.

CREDIBLE-ISH

But I thought the sign said, 'Parking? – Fine!'

Yes, I know it's illegal to park on double yellow lines, but these are quite definitely lemon.

After thirteen pints and a bottle of whisky for lunch, surely a man can be forgiven for thinking he was seeing a single yellow line twice?

The car's not taxed or insured, so I didn't think it would count.

Main street? Good Lord! I knew my reversing technique into the garage was getting a bit inaccurate, but this is ridiculous.

PRACTICALLY INCONCEIVABLE

Flood Prevention Unit, warden; my tyres are blocking the flow of rainwater to a dangerously overstressed drain.

A double yellow line? I just thought it was where some pavement artist had been cleaning his brushes.

I'm trying to give up my hardened crime addiction by cutting down gradually.

Tell me: how long have you been seeing imaginary vehicles parked at the side of the road?

I had this blinding flash of environmental responsibility and just had to pull over and save the world from my exhaust fumes.

I'm researching possible locations for the Dos and Don'ts section of the new Highway Code.

SUPRA-PARTY POLITICAL BROADCAST

Where do you expect the average motorist to park when hordes of inconsiderate pedestrians insist on walking on the pavement?

I was just seeing whether yellow stripes down the side of our driveway would match my wheeltrim.

Noise Abatement Society; I'm afraid this shade of yellow is just too loud to remain uncovered any longer, warden.

I'm training to be a foreign diplomat.

Are you mad? That car is precisely positioned to counterbalance stress along a major fault line, and thereby avert the possibility of earthquakes.

HAVEN'T I SEEN YOU ON JACKANORY?

You mean these yellow lines are *not* the slime trails of two migrating giant Chinese snails?

It's OK; I bought this kerbside from a man in the Crown and Anchor last Friday night.

I can't walk far; I'm a registered Idle Git.

At this point, for the sake of biographically inclined Bottomists, I think I should add a little PS, a sort of Priscilla Script. Personally, I've nothing against Priscilla the Hun. I could say she's mean, spiteful, intensely evil, and repulsive. But I don't go in for flattery. So, like the sweaty Crinkley Bottom office equipment rep, I'll stick to the fax – sorry, facts.

It all began in Crinkley Bottom one dark afternoon in 1945. Thunder tumbled through the heavens, the crack of mirrors rent the sky, and the little village was tossed from side to side by a light breeze. Suddenly, beneath the cardboard roof of a Crinkley Bottom house, from a downstairs loft came the sound of loose fish, and Priscilla the Hun (real name believed to be Marcos, Braun or Street-Porter) was born. Her mother preferred not to be present at the time, and her father, apparently an international golfer, was trapped in a bunker in Berlin.

Villagers began to suspect they were in for trouble when the doctor slapped Priscilla's bottom and broke four fingers, two of them not his own. It was probably his own fault; she was forty-six at the time. From those early beginnings, the thing that was beginning to become Priscilla the Hun began.

It started in a small way: nailing old Mrs Smalls's zimmer frame to the floor; gluing down the toilet lid at the Prune Addicts' Club; pulling the legs off spiders and sticking them back on the wrong way round. It moved on to telephoning the scientists in Crinkley Bottom's anthrax testing laboratory and shouting Boo; planting eighteen dumb-bells in twig-limbed Prudence Prendergast's shopping-bag; and making beep-beeping noises behind short-sighted villagers waiting at the pelican crossing.

Before she knew it, Priscilla was snipping the brake cables of villagers' prams, tying knots in local dachshunds, and calling up patients in Crinkley Bottom Hospital's Intensive Care Unit to tell them they'd won a dirty weekend with Susan Stranks.

But it didn't stop there. Steeped in evil, peevishness pulsating through her body like a bad curry, one black Thursday she callously and with malice aforethought telephoned me at the Great House and asked to borrow five pounds!

In that brief yet fiendishly reverse-charged phone call, it became clear that Priscilla was rollercoasting down the slippery slope towards the ultimate abomination. In the end, it was even worse. She became a traffic warden.

What led to this? Was her condition hereditary? Or did it get handed down to her by her parents? A famous top-secret Crinkley Bottom operation to dig up Priscilla's family tree uncovered her lineage in frank and startling detail:

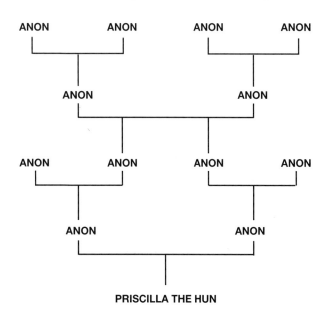

Although a little over 99.9 per cent of her forebears refused to be identified, Priscilla's family tree incorporated one significant feature lacking in that of the average Crinkley Bottomer – non-blood relations.

This was enough to set her apart. And so, shunned and despised, Priscilla stomped a solitary path through life, growing embittered, vindictive, and warts. Her next move was surprisingly inevitable: in an adjective-defying act of sheer demonic malevolence, she invented the Eurovision Song Contest.

Within weeks of her eighty-first fracture, local magpies had begun to salute her, and villagers were agreed that, while she was not the ugliest woman in Crinkley Bottom, she certainly looked like her.

For Priscilla now, the only way forward was back. In 1962, she formed the militant branch of Crinkley Bottom's Temperance Society and hijacked her first brewery lorry. Five weeks and

Priscilla, 1982: trying a little friendly persuasion

Priscilla, 1981: charm oozing from every scar

6,000 visits to the lavatory later, Priscilla abandoned virtually paid employment tutoring footballers for degrees in three-syllabic words, and took up organizing marches for CND – the Campaign for Nationwide Dismemberment. To all intents and purposes, Priscilla the Hun was now out of control. Nothing could hold her. Not that she'd have worn it if it could.

Before you could say jackboot, Priscilla had donned a traffic warden's uniform and embarked upon a campaign of parking law enforcement that was to strike terror into the hearts of every Crinkley Bottomer who'd ever pulled up in Snogging Bint Lane and popped into Mrs Bulstrode's for a pea.

The rest is history. Or rather, her story. Or maybe I was right first time, for Priscilla, who handles motorists with kid gloves made from real children, has never been known to fraternize with members of the opposite gender – possibly because no one's quite sure whether they are the opposite gender. What is certain is that Priscilla puts what passes for her heart into her work from the moment she launches herself on to the streets every morning, until the moment she catches the ambulance home every night.

Altercations on those streets are rare: the Crinkley Bottom motorist is the sort of timid creature who thinks valour's something you make hats out of. But Priscilla, who thinks a good turn is a well-behaved seagull, is the sort of woman who'd engender violence in a small nun; and over the years, she's acquired the injuries to prove it.

Her Three Limps are so famous they've become part of Crinkleyshire myths and legends – or perhaps that should be leg ends? Her celebrated Echoing Scar is the deepest in Crinkley Bottom since records failed to be kept. And word – in the form of my Great House butler Hal Green – has it that some of her bruises are as big as Belgium, and a heck of a sight more colourful. (How he knows, I'm not at liberty to divulge, so long as he keeps up the monthly unmarked envelopes.)

Attitudes towards Priscilla today are unequivocal: nobody has a bad word to say about her. They always try to think up a really obnoxious one. But maybe Priscilla has been misjudged. Maybe she's more sinned against than sinning. Maybe this is a fundamentally good, caring woman. Maybe Crinkley Bottom Wonderers is a successful football team, and the Liszt and Newt a haven of sense and sobriety.

No, take it from me, Bottomists, Priscilla the Hun is every evil inch the diabolically depraved empress of darkness she's been painted. And I would go on to expound further on the foulness of this despicable Crinkley Bottomer, but for two things. One, I'm a gentleman, and dislike making cheap and disparaging jibes at others' expense. And two, the disclaimer in this book about the characters bearing no resemblance to any persons living or dead – I'm not sure whether it covers traffic wardens.

Priscilla, 1983: the woman who put war into warden

10. Parish Mag

In the fluttering heart of the Crinkley Bottom Parish Magazine Office, the vicar of St Bottom's toils night and day to bring parish news to the attention of the village. In the Crinkley Bottom sub-post office, Fanny Smalls does it in a matter of minutes.

None the less, the Parish Magazine maintains a pre-eminent position in village life, partly because of its considered, informative articles and calm, rational advice, but mainly because it's free. And the cachet of having a letter published within its hallowed sheets is seen by villagers as an achievement on a par with leaving the Liszt and Newt without a mobility aid, or leaving Toepoker Park without a death wish.

Normally, it would fall to the vicar to throw light on Parish Magazine concerns. Sadly, he's currently under Doctor Fiddler, having suffered a great shock on finding a body in the church last Sunday – and an even greater one on finding it was alive. So, in his stead, his assistant editor, the verger, has kindly been volunteered to explain exactly how to get *your* letter published in the prestigious Crinkley Bottom Parish Magazine. Over to you, then, Bartholomew. This should be fascinating. Now, where's my 6,000-piece jigsaw ... ?

STAMPS

Easily acquired from the village sub-post office during its opening hour, stamps guarantee delivery of your letter nearly intact, reasonably cowpatsplash-free, and hardly read by Fanny Smalls, to a random address in the UK, within three months. Or years, in the case of second-class mail.

If you experience difficulty obtaining a stamp for your letter, try paying for it. This is important, because however cheap and convenient the alternative might seem, wrapping your letter round a brick, and lobbing it through our office window will not endear you to the vicar. And there's always the danger you'll miss his head and do some real damage.

STARTING

Chances of publication can be increased enormously by starting your letter.

LEGIBILITY

Look, we don't mind whether you've got a father or not. But if you can avoid ugly blots, smudges and Chinese, you could be on to a winner. Block capitals help, especially if you can get them in the right order. The villagers might not be able to read, but we suspect our printer can.

CONTENT

The vicar's relatively open-minded on content. As long as you mention *Songs of Praise*, *Thought for the Day*, and his name in the same sentence, you can write about almost anything you like. Try to lay off okapi snouts, treacle toffee and parachutes, though, for obvious reasons. And cut down on references to Eskimo architecture, post-Renaissance dentistry, and Poland before the glaciers; they've all been done to death in recent issues. Oh, and since he got copped poaching sea trout up at Sellafield, the vicar simply refuses to touch anything on nuclear fission.

AUTHENTICITY

If you're aiming for authenticity in your letter, this is how to spell it.

SHAKY HANDWRITING

Shaky handwriting is symptomatic of vitamin-B deficiency, senile dementia, or scribbling doctor's notes on the school bus: it doesn't fool anyone to claim it's the result of trying to pen us a missive while you're on your knees, fighting off the Liszt and Newt barmaid.

If you really want to make your letters look realistic, try a few Courvoisier stains in the margin. Better still, send me the bottle and I'll stain it for you.

NAMES

Names can be difficult, can't they? But don't sit up all night trying to remember yours. There are plenty about to choose from. So far this year we've had 400 Billy Butlins, 73 W.H. Smiths, 20 Mickey Mice, and a Terry Wogan. Or you could always use a pen name. Paper Mate and Bic are acceptable; Parker's more respectable, but we won't believe you. If you really are famous, though, please don't hesitate to tell us. It won't mean your letter will be published, of course, but you can be sure we'll flog your autograph for a fortune.

SCENT

Subtle, sweet nostril-loads of expensive perfume certainly add a little something to one's correspondence. Though exactly what, I'm dashed if I know. It's not as if the vicar's office hasn't got a big enough aerosol in it already.

But if you really feel life would lose all meaning without a whiff of scent on your deathless prose, be sparing, don't use a roll-on, and try to choose some fragrance that won't get up the vicar's nose: starched dog-collar, essence of buttered crumpet, sweating bridegroom, crucifix-brasso, font-scourer, cassock dubbin, and smoked choirboy are all highly appropriate, and guaranteed to blend in with the pervading office smog almost unnoticed.

FINISHING

It pays to finish your letter; we get it much quicker that way. But there's an art to ending all letters and in this case the trick is to stop writing before you run out of paper. Once you've mastered that, you can then pay attention to the finer points of signing off.

'Must rush now for the toilet' heralds the end of your letter in no uncertain terms, but it's not the sort of thing we want in a Parish Magazine, thank you very much.

'That's your lot', 'Wish you were here', and 'Cripes! here's the wife' are right out, too. 'Yours sincerely', 'Kind regards' and 'Wonderers for the Cup' are trite and obviously untrue. So I've devised a fair, simple, and honest valediction which will guarantee the publication of anyone's letter in our prized periodical: 'Loved the mag – keep up the good work. PS Here's a fiver.'

11. Up the Wonderers!

Say the name Wonderers in Crinkley Bottom, and you can be sure of a smile. In fact, most villagers would find it hard not to laugh. Even so, Crinkley Bottom Wonderers Very Amateur Football Club, nicknamed the Bluetits, have achieved widespread popularity (almost every team in Crinkleyshire wants to play them) and unparalleled experience (what they don't know about losing could be written on the back of a football stud).

Keenly indifferent to discover more, I hired my cassette recorder to local sports reporter Kenny Truss, and put him on the next haycart to Toepoker Park to probe the brains behind the Bluetits' revival, Tommy Toe-Poker. This is a verbatim transcript of that interview.

TRUSS: (*Fierce crackling*) ... doesn't seem ... working properly ... think ... dud batteries ... that nerd Edmonds .... hands on him ... strangle the little ... Ah! here we are.

(*A door opens.*)

TOE-POKER: Ah, Truss. You were supposed to be here an hour ago.

TRUSS: Sorry. I got lost. It was awfully embarrassing. I walked in on twelve naked men rolling around on the floor and laughing hysterically.

TOE-POKER: That would be the opposition changing room.

TRUSS: Funny. Someone said it was a Wonderers board meeting to discuss your future.

1956: Training:
Crinkley Bottom Wonderers'
first team practise not laughing
at one another's legs.

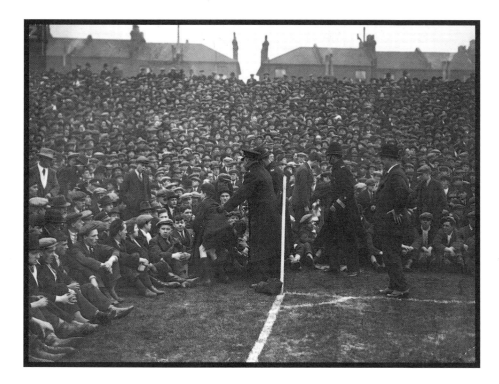

TOE-POKER: Nay, my future's secure here, lad. You've only got to look at the team's performance last season: remarkable achievement.

TRUSS: Why do you call finishing sixteenth a remarkable achievement?

TOE-POKER: There are only fifteen teams in the league.

TRUSS: Right. Tommy, I'd like to begin with a rather sensitive topic: the full back Willie Touchett.

TOE-POKER: Never heard of him.

TRUSS: He's your son-in-law.

TOE-POKER: Oh, that Willie Touchett. What about him?

TRUSS: Some people don't see him as a footballer. Maybe it's the way he brings a tennis racquet on to the pitch with him, or spends the half-time interval chalking up the end of the corner flag.

But it's being said he shouldn't be in the team, and you're being accused of nepotism.

TOE-POKER: Nonsense! I've never had anything to do with mind reading.

TRUSS: Are you saying no one gets employed by the 'Tits simply because they're related to the management?

TOE-POKER: Hypnotism, you mean? Definitely not. I remember when I first came here, the Chairman called me into his office, at the end of the canteen, and said, 'Tommy, I want no favouritism in this club on grounds of family ties. Any of that,' he said, 'and I'll disinherit you right away, son.'

TRUSS: That's good to hear. On a lighter note, Tommy, can I turn to your centre half, Choppem Off Titchmarsh? There's a view that he's – how can I put it? – a trifle boisterous.

45

TOE-POKER: Choppem Off – boisterous? Balderdash! He's a dirty swine, yes. But I'll say this for the lad: he was treated disgracefully in his last game against Dangley End Ramblers.

TRUSS: You didn't agree with the prison sentence, then?

TOE-POKER: Football's a rough game, Kenny. Centre forwards have to expect the odd ruptured spleen and multiple fracture.

TRUSS: Not when they're sitting at home watching TV twenty-four hours after the match.

TOE-POKER: So it was a late tackle. Is that any reason to lock the lad up?

TRUSS: Good point.

(*At this point, Toe-poker's telephone rings. In fine journalistic style, Truss averts his ears, and leaves the cassette recorder running.*)

TOE-POKER: Yes, operator, I'll accept the charges, but only if it isn't that Edmonds fool again ... Bobby! Hi ... Yes, I'm prepared to make you an offer. How's £300 sound? ... Well, there's no need to be – How much? ... Double? ... Look, you'll take £750 and like it, right? ... Fine. £900 it is, then. See you Saturday.

(*Toepoker replaces his phone. Truss mops up his tea The interview resumes.*)

TRUSS: Buying a player, Tommy?

TOE-POKER: Bribing a referee, lad.

TRUSS: You're joking, of course? (*Laughter.*)

TOE-POKER: (*Laughter*) No.

TRUSS: M-m-moving to the Bluetits' future: the players are full of confidence, obviously?

TOE-POKER: Are you taking the pistachio nut, lad? There's only one thing my players are full of, and it's not confidence.

TRUSS: But Bandy Coleman actually did a lap of honour after the last match.

TOE-POKER: That wasn't a lap of honour. He was trying to find his teeth. And, talking of deadbeats, don't talk to me about Troutneck Timpson.

TRUSS: He's the flanker, isn't he?

TOE-POKER: You can say that again. Old Trouty's got a problem with his shorts. He's drinking too many of them.

TRUSS: Surely there's some good news for the fans?

TOE-POKER: Oh, yes. They'll both be pleased to hear we're signing a new 'keeper from Nether Scratching Athletic.

TRUSS: When?

TOE-POKER: Just as soon as he can hold on to the pen long enough to sign his name. And our reserves were really unlucky yesterday. They lost 6–0 after leading 2–1 at half-time.

TRUSS: I hear you've also signed a new agreement with last season's sponsors.

TOE-POKER: That's right. They've agreed to pay us £5,000, and we've agreed not to put their names on our shirts again.

TRUSS: So the 'Tits go marching on. Well, thanks for your time, Tommy; I expect you'll want to start picking your side for the Crinkleyshire Cup now?

TOE-POKER: Already done it, lad. I've picked Dangley End Ramblers.

12. Employment Agency

People have often asked me to sum up Crinkley Bottom. I've tried to put it in a nutshell, but St Bottom's church spire keeps poking out of the top. The adjectives which most readily lurch to mind are sleepy, quiet, easy going, unhurried ... yes, I know what you're thinking: Can I get a job there?

Well, yes, you can. In fact, it's about time somebody did. No, that's not fair. Up at the Great House alone, I've got five villagers working for me; although I actually employ thirteen. And the thriving local job market is evident from a glance through the Sits Vac page of the *Crinkley Bottom Observer*, which only this week features advertisements for – let me see, page thirty-six,

next to the Readers' Letter, oh yes, here we are – Gelding Breeder's Assistant, Naturists' Dress Designer, Invisible Exports Shipping Agent.

Further down here, they're looking for a Family Planning Adviser at the Old People's Home; Crinkley Bottom Radio wants someone to help out in its subtitling department; and Terry Nutter needs a new person to walk his German Shepherd/baby Brontosaurus cross, and wipe up the old one.

The Pitz Cinema wants translators for its latest batch of silent French films. Crinkleyshire County Council needs an organizer for its indoor surfing weekend. And gorgeous blonde young model Clodaugh Bumpin-Melons has a vacancy

Hopeful Crinkley Bottom farm hands check local press for vacancies as professional pig shearers.

for a masseur: £800 a week – o.n.o.

An easier-to-swallow digest of posts is on display at Crinkley Bottom's Job Centre, through whose portals daily process the village's disillusioned, disheartened, deadbeat, derelict, and indolent. Or the staff, as they're more commonly known.

Queuing without at all hours of the mid-morning can be found a piggledy line of villagers, among them the de-aproned hairdresser Dianne Frizzett; Maurice Chinking-Jacket, freelance journalist and human drinks trolley; Mister Briggs, the understandably unemployed village brain surgeon; Thicky Nobwit, aspiring village idiot looking for work experience in local government; Basher Kickett, the perennially sacked TV repairman; and Mrs Bulstrode from the Pea Shoppe, who's not out of work; she just enjoys standing close to men in queues.

These are no representative sample of the village population, the majority of whom incline to the view that a career's something you put on the back of a bicycle to keep your shopping in. Nevertheless, under the guiding foot of its new lady director, Alison Wonderland, the Crinkley Bottom Job Centre has developed into a useful local service, providing job hunters with invaluable experience on how to queue, and somewhere to get out of the rain on weekday mornings.

Centre director Alison is undoubtedly an expert on jobs – she's had fifty-seven of them in the past three years – and her deputy ensures that everyone who comes to the Centre for benefit is guaranteed at least two weeks' full-time employment immediately – he gives them an application form to fill in.

In truth, the form isn't particularly difficult; it only has five questions (name, age, address, sex, and what's the diameter of Saturn's third moon to the nearest millimetre?), but Crinkley Bottom villagers have no regard for intellect. In fact, they don't like any Belgian football teams.

That's enough from me, though. All this talk of work's making me feel rather tired. I'm going to hand over to Alison, who's composed a definitive guide on employment in Crinkley Bottom. It's bound to be fascinating and compulsive reading. I hope the butler's put my hot-water bottle in ...

Hello, and thanks very much indeed, Noel. Noel? Has he gone? It's so hard to tell, isn't it? I hope he doesn't mind my calling him Noel: only, being involved with work, I've never actually come across him before. Surely he can't object to being called Noel, though, in view of the name other villagers call him. The only thing that can be said about that is that at least they get the number of letters right.

But back to employment hereabouts. I'd like to start with Crinkley Bottom's hi-tech, well-funded training centres. But, as there aren't any, I'm going to start with job-spotting.

JOB-SPOTTING

In employment, as in all other fields of subhuman endeavour, it's the early bird that catches the work. And early birds in Crinkley Bottom begin by poring over the Situations Vacant columns of our morning newspapers. Shrewder job-spotters wait for the evening paper, and cast a far-sighted eye down the Obituaries page.

Additionally, the chances of spotting a job here can be greatly enhanced by visiting our traditional places of work: offices, factories, building sites – you'll come to recognize them with practice. And you'll get plenty of that. Once there, check with the manager to see if he's looking for an extra pair of skilled, capable, willing hands. If he is, try to suggest someone who might be suitable. He'll be so excited by your naïvety, he'll probably take you on there and then.

APPLICATIONS

Once spotted, a job has to be applied for. It often surprises those villagers who haven't applied for work since the industrial revolution that even in Crinkley Bottom there are ways of doing this without leaving your self-esteem and trouser-knees in tatters. Crawling into a manager's office with your forelock clutched in one hand and a begging bowl in the other is not going to create the most favourable impression imaginable. You really must make an appointment first.

By far the best way of applying for a job in Crinkley Bottom is by letter. This won't necessarily give your prospective employer a better impression of your talents, but at least it will convince him you can write – a rare local skill – which can be an advantage if you're hoping to join one of our more literate professions, like the law, the civil service, and very occasionally journalism. Correct spelling, syntax and grammar are important if you want to be taken seriously by a Crinkley Bottom employer. If you're worried about any of these, slip a tenner into the envelope and he probably won't notice. Finally, all letters should be sent in writing. And addressing them to the correct department will ensure personnel attention.

APPEARANCE

Appearances are important. Having finally been asked to attend an interview here, your chance of acquiring the job can be improved by making one. It also helps if you're punctual. With luck, you'll be spending the rest of your working life arriving late, so it's only fair to turn up on time just once.

CLOTHES

Unless you're aspiring to be resident entertainer at the Crinkley Bottom Naturists' Society, you'll need clothes for your interview. A formal, matching jacket, waistcoat and trousers might not suit everyone, but well-cut clothes are only fitting if you're hoping to measure up. Fashionable, starched shirts can add a little collar to your life, and the correct footwear increases your socks appeal, especially if you're feeling down at heel. Always turn up properly turned out, and remember: you have a vested interest in your underwear as well.

DISPOSITION

On arrival in the village for your interview, you'll be tense, nervous and edgy. Don't be. An apprehensive interviewee is a failed interviewee. Despite the fact that you missed breakfast, missed the bus and caught the squitters, despite the fact that you patriotically blew your last forty quid on a pair of British-made shoes that are patriotically turning your toes red, white and blue, and despite the fact that the receptionist made you feel like a half-witted pariah with bad breath, bad teeth and bad taste, your prospective employer will expect you to be happy, smiling, cheerful and well able to get on with all strata of Crinkley Bottom society, from the lowest to the even lower. And while we're talking of Noel, why not study a video of the way he interacts and communicates with all members of the public. It pays to learn by others' mistakes.

THE INTERVIEW

Although they're playing golf at four, wanted on the phone by their mistress, and due to attend another blasted conference in the Bahamas first thing tomorrow morning, most Crinkley Bottom employers will magnanimously interrupt their hectic working schedules to grill the occasional fawning minion. After all, they need to know what they might be taking on, and it gives them something to laugh about in the club afterwards.

Most employers in Crinkley Bottom tend to be men. This is not their fault; it's just something they were born with. If, however, yours turns out to be a member of the opposing sex (your suspicions may be confirmed by a quick peep in her drawers – they'll be full of hairspray, Kleenex and old lipsticks), don't panic! Women are just as capable of making decisions as men. It just takes them longer. So be patient. With a little luck, she'll offer you a position. And if you're really good, she might even offer you a job as well.

REFERENCES

As references are the third thing you'll be asked for at a Crinkley Bottom interview – after your name and change for the coffee machine – it's sensible to have a stack of glowing reports ready to hand before you go in. If you've never had a job before, don't risk it. You'll have enough problems without having to explain away dubious credentials from spurious employers to sceptical interviewers.

SINCERITY

Putting yourself across as an open, truthful, trustworthy candidate for the job is an invaluable asset. Forget the make-believe references; if you can fake sincerity, you've got it made.

INTELLIGENCE

Acuity, ingenuity and immeasurable mental prowess are qualities a Crinkley Bottom interviewer always looks for in prospective employees. But as he's been interviewing local applicants for tortoises' years without detecting the merest glimmer, it's advisable not to startle him with anything that may be mistaken for intelligence. At best, he'll think you're deranged to apply for the job in the first place. At worst, you'll be seen as a threat to his and everyone else's job and tossed out by the testimonials before you can say clever dick.

Instead, strive for a high degree of mediocrity. It may be hard, but to get any job in Crinkley Bottom you have to persuade the interviewer that you're a marginally more attractive proposition than a bucket of plankton. Remember: the situation may be vacant, but this is no reason for you to be.

ENTHUSIASM

Crinkley Bottom employers like to see enthusiasm in a worker; it means he's earning them lots of money. Candidates should, therefore, learn to show boundless energy, eagerness and enthusiasm. Acting lessons help. So does Pedigree Chum. Try not to go over the top, though. Interview etiquette dictates that you refrain from demanding promotion until you've actually been employed.

QUESTIONS

Although the style and approach of many interviewers in Crinkley Bottom today is virtually indistinguishable from the blood-hungry medieval witch-finder, modern interviewees are at least granted certain privileges – such as a comfy chair, a telephone call to their lawyer and three questions to prove the incessant inquisition is not turning their healthy, inquiring minds into quivering blobs of Vaseline jelly.

In extreme circumstances, you'll be so terrified that your allotted span of questions will be quickly used up with desperate requests to visit the lavatory. In less fraught conditions, you'll be expected to impress the interviewer with safe, sensible inquiries about sales figures, training and pension plans. But to make a real impression on your future boss, you really only need to put one question: try asking him what he and his secretary were up to while parked in that secluded lay-by off the Dangley Road last Friday night.
The correct answer is the offer of a job for life, use of the executive loo, incredible perks and an unlimited expense account. Given the

intelligence of most Crinkley Bottom interviewers, you'll be surprised how quickly he comes up with it.

HOLIDAYS

Conditions of employment will be discussed in all Crinkley Bottom interviews; and holidays are one of the most important – they help you appreciate just how relaxing work is by comparison. Strangely, though, few employees are permitted extended periods of absence, in the hope that they'll eventually come to love their work. Two weeks a year, plus Bank Holidays and a dozen dear aunts' funerals are about the most you can seriously expect. So, despite your lifelong ambition to become a wine-soaked sofa sloth, be realistic in your demands for holidays: and at least wait until the interview's over before taking one.

ELEVENSES

It may transpire that your interview here coincides with your prospective employer's elevenses. This can happen at nine o'clock, ten o'clock, eleven o'clock, and three o'clock. And it probably will. It won't happen between twelve and three, as he's out to lunch; four o'clock's his time for golf; and he's always home by five. Except on Fridays.

If you're lucky enough to be offered tea and the opportunity to nibble the boss's ginger nuts during your interview, by all means do so. Should you be accepted for the post, you sure as heck won't get the chance again.

JUSTIFICATION

At some stage in the interview, your interviewer
will decide he needs a laugh; so he'll ask you why
you'd like to join the company. This is a trick
question. If you're truthful, and tell him it's
because you've heard the office party makes
Sodom and Gomorrah look like Trumpton, you'll
be shown the door with no little haste. If, on the
other hand, you lie through your fillings, and tell
the old fool it's because you're seeking an outlet
which will stretch your immense vocational
capabilities to the very limit and you've heard
Crinkley Bottom companies offer the decent,
talented and conscientious worker boundless
exciting opportunities, he'll be taken in and you'll
be taken on like a shot. Where business success in
Crinkley Bottom is concerned, honesty is not only
not the best policy: it's a policy no one's even
heard of.

SALARY

Village salaries are like Wonderers' away goals –
you get one every month. If you're lucky.
Consequently, salary negotiations tend to follow a
well-trodden path. You, as the prospective
employee, explain why you, your wife, your fifty
children and your twelve terminal dear aunts a
year believe you deserve to be paid a mind-
boggling sum. He, as the prospective employer,
explains why he, his secretary, his fifty
accountants, and his termagant board of directors
believe you're only worth half as much. You choke
and look shocked. He smiles and looks at his
watch. You point out that times are hard, and
couldn't he just pay an extra –? He points out that
time's pressing, and no. You sigh; he looks at his
watch; you grit your teeth, accept defeat – and
vow things will be a darn sight different next
time. They won't. But we all need our dreams.
Especially when we're working in Crinkley
Bottom.

13. A Journey around Mrs Bulstrode

Get yourself out one morning to Hampton Rise, and you can usually hear it: squelch! squelch-squelch! squelch! squelch! squelch-squelch! squelch!

At first, it sounds like some pizza-cheeked old farmer gruffling* his way up to Muckflirter's Meadow across Gobbit Bog. Then you listen harder – squelch! squelch-squelch! squelch-squelch-squelch! – and you think, nah, the village idiot's been trying to mend his shoes with chewing-gum again.

You're not even close.

It's Mrs Bulstrode from the Pea Shoppe. Hold on, don't go making up your own jokes. When I say it's Mrs Bulstrode, I don't mean it's her exactly. It's her cats. Or, rather, it was.

I'll start again.

Mrs Bulstrode from the Pea Shoppe has got a lot of cats. Multitudinous cats. Gannet beaksful of them. In fact, her home at No. 42 Newt Welders Walk is so full of cats that any burglar hoping to break in would need chain-mail

Mrs Bulstrode's finer felines

* Gruffle is a Crinkley Bottom colloquialism, meaning to galomph, to lubbersnug, or to promknicker in an extremely snodgerous manner.

shinguards. But, no matter how impregnable No. 42 is from the outside, the furry occupants within never find any difficulty getting out. By dawn, Newt Welders Walk looks like the scene of a major Kattomeat strike, and sounds like a ripe-sock collectors' convention. And it smells about the same.

As morning progresses, so the cats too move on, driven by a mysterious innate wanderlust and Terry Nutter's German Shepherd/baby Brontosaurus cross, out of Newt Welders Walk to other, more fragrant Crinkley Bottom thoroughfares.

Crinkley Bottom is a small village – the local policeman only qualifies for a unicycle – and the roads tend to be relatively quiet. It's the cars that make the noise. Even so, between 8.30 and 9 a.m., even Crinkley Bottom motorists are moving a bit lickety-splitally around the village. And, coincidentally enough, it's at precisely this time that Mrs Bulstrode's cats make their morning exodus from Newt Welders Walk.

If you've never witnessed a cat–car collision, I can tell you it's not a pretty sight. There is wild screeching, torn hair, frightfully piercing whining. And that's just the driver when he sees the damage to his paintwork. As for what it does to the cats, well, as I said, get yourself out one morning to Hampton Rise, and you can usually hear it: squelch! squelch-squelch! squelch! squelch! squelch-squelch! squelch!

Nobody's sure exactly how many cats Mrs Bulstrode owns. All we know is that it's about a dozen fewer every day. To say she gets annoyed at the perpetrators is like saying the Joker gets a bit miffed with Batman. And at eighteen stone, with muscles born of carrying around twenty-four cats on her shoulders all weekend, it's advisable not to get on the wrong side of Mrs Bulstrode. In fact, don't get on any side of her, unless the wind's in the right direction.

Lamentably, however, no matter how careful you are on your travails around Crinkley Bottom, you'll find it practically impussible not to hurt Mrs Bulstrode's finer felines. So, here are twenty purrfect excuses which, although they won't help you avoid her cats, will at least help you dodge her left hook and about six months in traction.

20. The cat simply wasn't looking where I was going.
19. I thought it was bluffing.
18. I thought it was a traffic warden.
17. I just wanted to save it the trouble of suddenly jumping out in front of me.
16. I'm a member of the ultra-radical Mouse Liberation Front.
15. It's not as if it moved about much before, is it?
14. I just thought it would appreciate a closer look at my revolutionary new transerve tungsten-carbide flange-sprocket system.
13. For heaven's sake, it's only dead.
12. The cat was clearly headed for a meal at the Crinkley Café: I was doing it a kindness.
11. You expect them to do a handspring over the bonnet, or duck or something don't you?
10. When they've got nine lives you don't think these sort of things will matter.
 9. What do you expect when you insist on keeping a tarmac-coloured cat?
 8. It was too late when I realized they were the wrong kind of cat's eyes.
 7. The cat was obviously drunk.
 6. I flashed my headlights, and slowed to

120, but the cat just didn't notice.

5. I just wanted to see if it would land on its feet.

4. It was either your cat, or one-two-hundred-and-fiftieth of a millimetre of my brake linings: no contest.

3. You wouldn't think a rubber wheel could do that sort of damage.

2. It was suicide.

1. I suffer from cat-blindness.

Right, now we've disposed of her cats, so to speak, I'd like to go more deeply into Mrs Bulstrode. Oh, come on, please! We can do without the sniggers. I'm touching on a very delicate area of Mrs Bulstrode here. Right! That's it! You, you, you, and you – get out of this book and don't come back until you've learned to stop tittering. And you – out!

That's better. Now: Mrs Bulstrode. Superficially, she is the epitome of a Crinkley Bottom villager: upright, indomitable, ugly; the sort of woman who put the wart in stalwart.

Physically, she's ample – with six exclamation marks. If they made a film out of this book, Mrs Bulstrode would be played by Greenland. She's so large, her first husband was convicted of bigamy; and, as one of the few human beings ever to possess an epicentre, it's said the only part of her body that doesn't wobble when she walks is her big toenail. Frankly, I can't see it myself. And neither, I imagine, can she.

In her favour, Mrs Bulstrode's arms go just far enough down to reach her hands, and her ears are precisely the right distance apart to fit her head between them.

Psychologically, Mrs Bulstrode (first name known only to two close friends and 386 members of His Majesty's Royal Crinkleyshire Bombardiers) lives in the past. She finds the people are so much nicer there. Consequently, she's an old-fashioned sort – donkey-stones her doorstep, irons dusters, talks back to people on the television, tuts instead of swearing, hoards paper bags, polishes windows with the tip of her tongue sticking out, wears hats – usually no more than one at once, and says things like it's five-and-twenty to four, even when it isn't.

In the dark, primitive, pagan days of Crinkley Bottom's future, Mrs Bulstrode would be the sort of village wise woman, dispensing old Crinkley Bottom sayings and home-spun philosophy to anyone intrepid enough to plunge a groat into her puddingy palm. In these less enlightened times, one merely has to pass the Pea Shoppe to cop an earful of it:

People who live in glass houses shouldn't throw parties

Where there's life, there's a double-glazing salesman

The road to Hell is paved with good inventions

A fool and his money are soon married

A closed mouth gathers no feet

Appearances can be defective

Travel broadens the behind

Rome wasn't burnt in a day

Cleanliness is next to impossible

All's fair in love and Scandinavia

A problem shared is tempting blackmail

Two's company, three's a Liberal Democrat rally

Never put off today what you can put off tomorrow

The shortest distance between two points is still too far

Where's there's muck, there's someone scraping his shoe on a wall.

– The fruits of Mrs Bulstrode's experience. And she's certainly had plenty of both – fruit and experience, not to mention fruity experience. Don't look at me like that; it's perfectly true. In the days before she was only allowed on to Crinkley Bottom's streets on alternative days of the week, Mrs Bulstrode was known as the woman who put the fat into femme fatale. Indeed, I have it on the authority of my butler Hal Green, the Reuter's of local village life, that Mrs Bulstrode once appeared in a Bounty advert. Admittedly, it was as the desert island, but that's not the point. Mrs B, known to her many paramours as 'Bliss' Bulstrode, was, not to mince words, quite a girl.

Her adolescence was spent going to parties in her best frock. (Actually, that's not wholly true; some of the smaller ones were held in the village hall.) And when war broke out, plucky, nationalistic Miss Bulstrode made a man out of half Crinkley Bottom's male population. With a little more time, she might have made two men out of them.

Hal himself one night became so smitten by La Bulstrode's charms, he poetically offered her his 'pumping organ'. It wasn't until he regained consciousness in Crinkley Bottom's Intensive Care Unit that Mrs Bulstrode realized he'd meant his heart. And Hal realized he hadn't.

Thereafter, Hal Green vowed to have nothing further to do with women, and got engaged to Prudence Prendergast of the Wool Shop. Their lifelong conjunction of mind, soul and salary lasted about four and a half weeks, before it was wrecked on the stormy waves of the Beast of Tiddler's Lake affair (q.v.).

For her part, if you'll pardon the expression, HMS *Bulstrode* steamed on through life, fickle as a butterfly, albeit many hundredweight heavier. In 1959 she took an apt interest in the campaign to Save the Whale, only

to be thrown out when it became clear she just wanted to save it for breakfast.

Dalliances followed with many of Crinkley Bottom's young bloods: Warren Peace, Nick R. Elastic, Soldier Ron, I.B. Fuddled, OR, and Horace Peebey were just a few of those not to have paid me a tenner to keep my mouth shut. Others who didn't include the romantic failure Slosher Collins, who just wants to be loved for what he might have been; Lanky Chegwin, professional dilettante and moth boy, who never wears one anorak when two will do; the mint-owning Tiny Blackburn, Fishmonger of the Year in 1985; Clarence 'Ole Cross Eyes' Sinatra, the ninety-three-year-old office junior, who once believed a weather forecast; Lofty Corbett, whose wife was repossessed when his cheque for the marriage licence bounced; Twaddler MacCaskill, alternative toyboy and desert collector; Lurgy Ogden, who changed his mind in the middle of a sex-change operation and became the village odd ball; Benjamin Fiddler, an expert in the study of simple prehistoric life forms, better known as the Crinkley Bottom doctor; leg entrepreneur Chunky Manilow, who imported 6,000 white knee socks in 1962 and is still trying to find 3,000 people with white knees to sell them to; and Snotty Pratt – Gracie Fields stumbled against his nose in 1940 and he hasn't blown it since.

Yes, for Mrs Bulstrode, the *extra-*terrestrial, it was quite a week. And it was, inevitably, during this interlewd that her name became linked with the midnight skinny-dipping in St Bottom's church scandal. Please! Do try to gasp a little more plausibly. For new Bottomists, the midnight skinny-dipping in St Bottom's church scandal involved 23 men, 132 tubes of glue, a pair of stepladders, 50 feet of rope, and a winch. And that was just to rebuild the font afterwards.

The fall-out was earth-shattering. Crinkley Bottom is a strait-laced society. Villagers do no work at all on Sundays – and even less during the rest of the week; chimney breasts remain covered in spring; and local girls aren't allowed out at weekends without a chaperone. On Friday, you can see them all heading off to the hat shop to buy one.

The weight of village disapproval was brought to bear on Mrs Bulstrode. She was given two choices: zip up, or ship out. Cowed, sheepish, and probably not wishing to wait fourteen and a half months for the next bus to Dangley End, Mrs Bulstrode succumbed.

She plumped for a life of zippered propriety, caring for the cats she believes to be the reincarnated souls of her lost loves, and long-sufferingly explaining to dancing visitors to her village store that the Pea Shoppe is not a lavatorial euphemism.

Happily, it is not for her amatory or anatomical fecundity that Mrs Bulstrode is renowned in Crinkley Bottom. This lady and three-quarters owns a far more extraordinary claim to fame, for it was she who, returning home one night from a game of Spot the Brain Cell at the Crinkley Bottom Council AGM, made the famous 1958 sighting of the Beast of Tiddler's Lake. Look, if that's the best you can do, let's just forget about gasping altogether, shall we? This was the

Mrs Bulstrode's beastly experience

initial sighting of the legendary Beast, made all the more important because it was also the first.

Mrs Bulstrode's original impression was of a distinct stink: sweet, floral, almost like perfume. Then, as the twilight shrewdly fled before her, she perceived a huge, humped, moon-pink back, rising and falling rhythmically from the reeds at the northern end of the lake.

Mrs Bulstrode probed on. Though dusk and her bring-and-buy sale spectacles made vision difficult, she detected a pale white throat, two pairs of rear legs, several flailing arms, and a sort of circular swinging vertebrae appendage, uncannily reminiscent of a string of pearls. Sundry unoccupied items of female clothing clung to adjacent bushes, as though the Beast had feasted off some hapless local maiden and spat out the yukky bits.

Then, without warning, a lung-wracking grunt burst from the reeds and goosed the night air.

Panic gripped Mrs Bulstrode, and was promptly awarded the Victoria Cross for bravery. Meanwhile, news of the sighting spread through the village like dog poop on the postman's shoe. Pandemonium reigned: the Crinkley Bottom Council met; questions were asked; several members even woke up. Alas, no answer forthcame, and the sighting of the Beast of Tiddler's Lake remains to this day unexplained.

Yet possibly the real mystery is why the Reverend Dews and Prudence Prendergast who, on their own admission, spent the entire evening around Tiddler's Lake, failed to spot either the Beast or – even more incredibly – Mrs Bulstrode.

Pru, forty-two at the time although probably not as old as that now, and Dews, Vicar of St Bottom's and the Paranoid Club's pencil-top taster, were in the area on a mission for the ANC, or Association of Newt Counters. (They established, incidentally, that 48 per cent of Crinkley Bottom's newt population were to be found in Tiddler's Lake. The remaining 52 per cent were split evenly between the Winking Nun's snug and the Crinkley Café's fish-paste sandwiches.)

Speaking on the night of the sighting, Pru, dishevelled after her newt hunt but fragrant as ever, swore by her pearls that she had neither seen nor heard – or indeed smelt – anything untoward all evening. Dews, the white of his dog collar blending Gaelically with the orange of his cheeks and the green of his trousers' knees, backed her up to the hilt.

So – the white throat, the pearly appendage, the animated limbs, the pistoning back – was it all just a hoax? Mrs Bulstrode says no, it didn't look like any kind of tree. Thus, the mystery persists; confusing, curious, contradictory; just awaiting someone with a little wit and ingenuity to solve it. And that, in turn, raises yet another mystery: where on earth are we going to find anyone with wit and ingenuity in Crinkley Bottom?

14. Into the Barely Known

Crinkley Bottom has a dark secret. No, it's nothing to do with the parachute, treacle toffee and strap-on okapi snout which Mrs Bulstrode from the Pea Shoppe saw being delivered to the vicarage in a giant padded parcel – although what the vicar wanted with treacle toffee, and how Mrs Bulstrode came to be in a giant padded parcel, remains a mystery to this day.

No, Crinkley Bottom's dark secret is darker than even that. We're talking real moles' toenails here. In fact, I'm not really sure I should be revealing it in a work of obvious literary merit, or indeed a tome brimming with wit and pith (and thankfully successful proof-reading). But as this book is neither of those, I don't suppose it matters.

You see, it's all to do with parts. The world sees my Crinkley Bottom, and thinks: a bit rough and ready, maybe, but chirpy and chumful enough; definitely somewhere you could release your mother-in-law back into the wild without case-hardening her corsets.

What few people realize is that there are two sides to my Crinkley Bottom; one of them dark and secret, referred to only in hushed voices down fear-clad alleys by men with frightened eyes and jibbering kneecaps. It is, in a word, Upper Bottom. All right, it's two words. Everyone's got to be so picky.

Upper Bottom is a district of Crinkley Bottom, lying between Nibbler's Nook and the Venus De Milo Arms. Normal folk don't go there. Animals whimper and turn back at its borders. Birds take the long way round. It's a heck of a place to ride out a fatwa.

At least, it would be if it weren't for the residents. Because, well, let's be honest; no point covering these things up, they're – posh. Sorry. I don't often use such shocking four-letter words, but this one's really justified in the case of Upper Bottomers.

Talk about show-offs! They're the sort of

The Snootie-Burkes of Upper Bottom: two of everything, except friends

people who leave the lights on when they're not moving around. They've got punctuation marks in their graffiti, and loo paper you can't read.

They eat crisps with a knife and fork, and throw away unpatched teabags. They get their garden manure delivered in bags, rather than bringing it home unexpectedly on the bottom of a shoe!

Upper Bottom adolescents crook their little fingers while vandalizing phone boxes; burglars send thank-you notes; and visitors always take their shoes off before putting their feet up on the table.

Some really élite Upper Bottomers even colour-coordinate their nail varnish to match their daily activities: blue for swimming, brown for sunbathing, and green for picking their noses. And the women are even worse.

Hardly surprising, then, that ordinary villagers driving past Upper Bottomers in the street wind down their electric windows, and call out, 'Swankers!' At least, I think that's what they call out.

But hold on a minute here.

Are we really such a blinkered, bigoted, nasty, peevish lot that we can't tolerate someone who considers him or herself superior to us?

All right, let me put it another way. Half the Crinkley Bottom Golf Club Committee is made up of Upper Bottomers, and if some of us are going to stand a chance of sinking a short one at the nineteenth this side of a bus pass, we must start talking to Upper Bottom soon.

The topics don't have to be imaginative – the weather, the traffic, the reasons why I should be awarded free life-membership of the Golf Club will do fine.

Course, it won't be easy communicating with people who talk as though they've got plastic adenoids and Munchees for brains; so here's an extract from my seminal English–Upper Bottom Phrase Book. In it, you'll find all the words necessary to talk to the sadly misunderstood and much maligned Upper Bottomer. Now, all you've got to do is find one sane and sober enough to talk back.

Upper Bottom's lady Philippa Yoyo-Bloomers barely known by 370 villagers last New Year's Eve

FREIGHT: A sudden shock, or a type of cocktail.

DI: 24 hours, or an old school friend who married well.

DRINKY-POOH: An intoxicating beverage, popular in Upper Bottom, where its constituents are generally nine parts alcohol, one part bloodstream. Also a synonym for foreplay.

WAIT WAYNE: A type of drinky-pooh, used to disguise the taste of fish.

CLAYS: Garments.

KIZE: That jolly boating week on the Ale of Wait.

FISSION: One of Upper Bottom's most popular outdoor pursuits, along with hauntin', shootin', and banging one's Merc door at 3.45 a.m.

HAND: A hauntin' man's best friend. Most varieties have five legs: four on the ground, and one in the mouth.

EIGHT: Not in.

CHARS: A toast, or those freightfully fanny women who calm and clane one's hise.

SHEEZATREZ: A char who works for nothing.

FEATHER: The husband of one's Murmarh.

PA: What drives one's electric toothbrush or one's political ambitions.

WORK: An occupational hazard.

HEIGHT: Intense dislike, or something worn on Ladies Di at Escort.

HAIR: In the song, where one comes as a bride.

COSH: A volga method of settling one's accaints.

EXCESS COD: A sooper method of not settling one's accaints.

SWEATER: An Upper Bottom bank manager.

GATE: A hardy four-legged beast bred for cardigans.

YARSE: Provisionally, yes, but only if it won't cost me money.

A PAIR OF JEANS: Two small intoxicating drinky-poohs, also known as lunch.

ACE: An incompetent person, or the cold lumpy bits in one's jeans.

ADA CLARKE: The hour before one is due to arrive late for work.

WAIF: A single woman whose divorce hasn't quite worked out.

BED: The black pointy thing one's psychiatrist has on his chin.

LARVA: An immature creature designed to fill the gaps between husbands.

EXERCISE: Jogging to one's cocktail cabinet.

MILD EXERCISE: Watching one's butler jog to one's cocktail cabinet.

CELERY: A freightfully useful thing one can swap each month for drinky-poohs.

SHAH: An investment, or what one washes one's poodle under.

MAYOR: An unwontedly polite request, normally employed when seeking something of immense personal value, as in 'Mayor have another drinky-pooh?'

BARKS: What one watches when one really should be at the opera.

POSH: What one's other car is.

LEGWARMERS: One's matching Siamese cats.

LABEL: Inclined to, as in, 'After drinky-poohs, one's label to feel merry.'

MERRY: A close female friend.

CARD: A freightened person, or an offally fanny playwright, first names Sar Narl.

PARLOUR: A game played by horses with sticks and men.

RAGGER: A game for spectators, played by men with fanny-shaped balls.

RIDING: What one spends one's mornings doing to the gossip columns to discover what one got up to last night.

SAD WITCH: A DIY comestible packed in Upper Bottom picnic hampers to stop the bottles of drinky-pooh rattling.

LOCAL CHARACTER: A lower-class villager.

COLOURFUL LOCAL CHARACTER: A lower-class villager with grey hair, brown teeth and yellow toenails.

SEX: What one has one's potatoes delivered in.

AREN'T: A female relation.

GREAT AREN'T: A fat female relation.

DEAR AREN'T: A rich female relation.

ANKLE: The husband of one's aren't.

AUNTY: What one does to one's shoelaces at bedtime.

ISSUE: A noise made by an Upper Bottomer with 'flu.

OYSTER: A religious holiday marked by fanny heights and chocolate eggs.

AIR CONDITIONER: What lower-class ladies put on their hair after the shampoo.

URDU: A lower-class lady's perm.

PIETY: A celebratory gathering with drinky-poohs, cake and sad witches.

CAKE: A white substance taken at all the best pieties.

BAYONET: What one's personal mechanic raises to get at one's Merc engine.

PURLOIN: What one finds Upper Bottom motorists doing to their caravans.

THURSDAY: What one gets when one hasn't had a drinky-pooh for absolutely minutes.

AVNOTUSHEDADROFFSHER: I've not touched a drop, officer.

BARN: A three-year job opportunity for a chauffeur.

15. Pitz

Anyone looking for a good night out in Crinkley Bottom should consider the Pitz Theatre and Cinema Centre. Then go somewhere else.

Because the Crinkley Bottom Players, whose home that is, aren't what they were in the old days. And they were pretty awful even then.

The Pitz's publicity manager

The gnarled oaken name plate which swung like eyeballs at Wimbledon below the Pitz sign (the R became a P in Hurricane Fish several years ago, and villagers felt the new title was just too appropriate to repair) has gone, replaced by a swanky brass plaque bearing the epithet Miracle Repertory Company, beneath which some anonymous hand has penned the phrase, 'If it's a good play, it's a miracle.' Everyone wants to be a critic.

It's sad, since, in its heyday, you could stroll around the Pitz of an evening, and be deafened by the fat throatfuls of laughter within. And it was even worse when they were putting on a comedy. Now the only laughter you hear is when the usherette tells someone the price of a choc ice.

I blame the plays they put on. All this 'Cor! That's a Big 'Un, Vicar', and 'There's a Girl In My Trousers', and 'No Beans, Please; I'm Airborne': it's all too highbrow for the average Crinkley Bottomer.

The Pitz itself is worth a visit, though. At least, the Crinkleyshire Pest Control Officer seems to think so. So why not grab your donkey jacket and your best wellies (the gents can come as they are), and come with me on a spangled, no economies spared tour of downtown Crinkley Bottom's entertainment-land.

As we sweep through the door, using a nifty bit of footwork to avoid the dead rat on the step, our attention is instantly snatched by the correspondence on the foyer wall: letters from major international celebrities, all framed and polished, and all apologizing for their inability to attend one of the Miracle Repertory Company's opening nights. Awed and humbled, we cast a boggling eye along the slightly dubious excuses:

'I'm washing my hair.' – Warren Mitchell

'I'm ironing my jeans.' – Bob Geldof

'I'm answering my fan mail.' – Edwina Currie

'I'm addressing a temperance meeting.'
– George Best

'I'm seeing an older woman.' – Bill Wyman

'Something unexpected came up.' – Russell Grant

'I try to avoid being seen in public.'
– Linda Lusardi

'I'm having an early night.' – Oliver Reed

'I'm calculating next year's fare reductions.'
– The Head of British Rail

'I'm taking on new workers.' – The Head of British Coal

'I'm taking a girlfriend out.' – Julian Clary

'I'm doing something normal.' – Prince Charles

'I've simply nothing to wear.'
– The Princess of Wales

'I've been invited to a barmitzvah.'
– Yasser Arafat

'I've got an appointment at the Family Planning Clinic.' – The Pope

'I can't afford the bus fare.'
– The Duke of Westminster

'It's my aerobics class.' – Jockey Wilson

'I'm packing for my British tour.' – Ronnie Biggs

'I'm going out.' – Salman Rushdie

'I'm staying in.' – Sir Ranulph Fiennes

'I'm engaged.' – Cliff Richard

'I've got a lot on.' – Cher

'I've got tickets for a Madonna concert.'
– Mary Whitehouse

'I'm organizing an anti-blood sports rally.'
– Prince Philip

'I'm studying for my Metaphysical Science degree.' – Michaela Strachan

'I'm celebrating my birthday.' – Joan Collins

Moving through the foyer into the auditorium, we, we – what? ... Don't be ridiculous. Do you know who I am? ... Noel Edmonds ... Well, there's no need to be like that about it – we are steered back by the commissionaire to the box office, where a lady sells us tickets for the upper circ—how much? – front stalls.

Back in the auditorium, it's touching to see how many villagers have travelled all this way to dispose of their empty Coke cans.

The interior here owes much to Italian architecture: the doors have been nicked from La Scala, and the curtain was a job lot of old hassock covers from the Vatican. There's history here; three centuries too much of it, according to the structural surveyor's report. One can see his point. And so can I. The ceiling holds a unique place in British theatre, in that there's more of it on the

The Pitz: another smash on its hands

ground than up in the roof. The floor moves around more than the scenery. And the auditorium is lined with what can only be described as dirty, green, muckswilly* old cheese lumps – although the technical term for them is walls.

The building's shaky condition places one or two constraints on the audience, who now bring their own hard hats, and take it in turn to clap (the left half of the theatre usually does it in January; the right half, at the end of July). Eating popcorn has been banned as it is likely to bring the house down faster than anything the Players can put on: although older patrons can still buy the stuff, on condition they leave their teeth as deposit.

Naturally, the Government has been approached for financial help. In '86, cinema manager Chubby Attenborough cited the Pitz's

aesthetic and artistic qualities as justification for an Arts Council grant. And it worked! They offered him £6,000 to pull it down.

But this is still a fine, upstanding venue. Well, a fine, nearly upstanding ven – not so – nue. And, tip-toeing down the aisle, forgoing the breeches buoy provided, we are surrounded by sites of worldwide local interest. There's the back row, fêted and fetid, where teenaged couples traditionally sit for obvious reasons, namely that they won't have so far to walk when they get chucked out.

Over there – no, there, past the nettles, by the puddle – we see seats P13 and 14, immortalized in the annals of village surgery one evening in June '85 when eager young lothario Snorky Paxman french-kissed Doris Deep-Ear Dunant with a pound of Bazooka Joe bubblegum

* Muckswilly: Crinkley Bottom colloquialism for wet, sodden, salty. Derived from the verb muckswill, meaning to fall off a yacht, or steal a pension fund.

on his tongue and removed half her tonsils.

We pause alongside row M, minded of that day when the Crinkley Bottom Players received their last standing ovation. What was it – two, three decades ago? What a pity the local loan company doesn't come to repossess the seats every week.

Further down, oh dear! someone's left his lunch on seat 5, row D. Well, at least he had the satisfaction of eating it first. Chubby's obviously been showing his horror films again.

Swiftly on to the backstage, and we can really feel the magic of show business here – which is lucky, because in this lighting, we'd be hard-pressed to see it.

Opening a door, we're eyesmacked by a sparkling fruit-print dress, peeled off and sprawling exhausted on a chair. Tumbled over it and twinkling in the candlelight lies a sequinned blouse, a sheer silver bodystocking – sadly empty, a lurex leotard decorated with more colours than a parrot in a blender, stiletto thigh-boots, white knee socks, and a – white knee socks, fwor! – and a pair of fluffy blue shoulder pads, suitable for anyone with a pair of fluffy blue shoulders.

Freshly washed chorus-line stockings dangle under a mantelpiece like strands of mucus from a wintry nostril, weighted by a mini-metropolis of jars and bottles of rouge, Leichner, pancake, face cream, greasepaint, scent, and mascara.

Together, they form the typical paraphernalia of a busy modern actress's dressing-room. Strange we should find them in the cinema manager's office.

Should've guessed, really. The Pitz's dressing-rooms aren't nearly so sumptuous, as will become evident as we open this rather narrow door, marked 'Dressing Ro', on to a four-walled space that's so small it's only got three corners. The interior's uncluttered, though, with central seating facilities and running water; and it's perfectly practical, if you can avoid knocking the toilet roll off when you turn ar— whoops!

Oh! and look here: doubtless to foment interest in the Wool Shop, Prudence Prendergast has written her telephone number on the wall. How industrious that woman is.

Across the corridor resides the true seat of power. This is the room used by the exalted and much loved brains behind the Crinkley Bottom Players, evidenced by the word 'Projuicer' chalked on the door, next to the dagger and dart holes.

Inside, we find everything a producer needs to bring his play smoothly from conception to performance. But apart from the whisky bottle, there's also a megaphone, a couch – twin-berth, jackboots, and a script of his latest production, together with the crayon he used to write it.

In days of yore, this used to be the changing-room of Crinkley Bottom's famous music-hall stars the Three Ronnies – Ronnie Axson, Ronnie Birtles, and Geoff White. Great comedy, hopeless arithmetic. Little remains from that era – Arthur 'Houdini' Little, Crinkley Bottom's escapologist, to give him his full stage name. Although he, too, will be leaving, just as soon as someone comes to untie him.

Yes, the Miracle Repertory Company's glory days are at an end. And so, I think, it's only fitting that we now cease our probing, draw a discreet curtain over this sorry scene, leave this once noble building to what little self-respect it has left, and – here, what's this? In the bottom drawer of the producer's desk, the secret one with the combination lock and booby trap: it's a list of forthcoming productions. Talk about cutbacks! Look at this:

Seven Brides for Three Brothers

Puss in Bare Feet

Lady Chatterley's Inflatable Doll

Joseph and His Amazing Technicolor Duffel Coat

Cat on a Warm Tin Roof

The King and IOU

Half a Sixpence – Or Two Pee for Cash

The Sound of Muzak

The Hamster of the Baskervilles

Murder on the Orpington Express

Guess Who's Coming to Elevenses

A Comedy of Arrears

Debt in Venice

Last Tango in Powys

Begging Letter to Brezhnev

Clearly, things are worse than we imagined. Poor old Crinkley Bottom Players: derided, ridiculed, mocked, ignored, and now impecunious, insolvent, humiliated, broke and broken. Still, I suppose it might have been worse. They could have been cast in *Brookside*.

Talking of money, I wonder how much they'd take for those white knee socks ...?

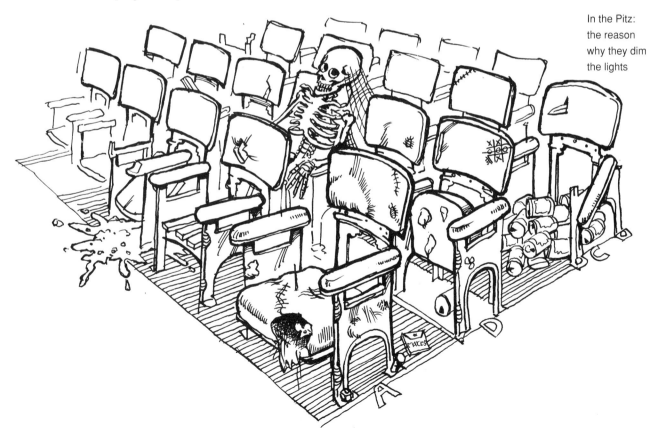

In the Pitz: the reason why they dim the lights

16. Mad Ads

YOUR GUIDE TO THE GOODS, SERVICES AND OPPORTUNITIES AVAILABLE IN CRINKLEY BOTTOM DIRECT FROM THE CRINKLEY BOTTOM OBSERVER'S CLASSIFIED PAGES (20P A WORD, OR 5P IF THEY DON'T HAVE TO LOOK IT UP IN THE DICTIONARY).

CRINKLEY BOTTOM OBSERVER   14 June 1936

Make your hedgehog safe

Eliminate third party insurance claims and the possibility of flat tyres with our unique individual spine tip protectors. Slip on or lace up style, in flexible long lasting rubber. Monogram option. please state colour and number of spines.

Improva pet, ltd box 31.

Exceptionally small-boned people required to reach into cassette players and pull out ravelled up tapes. Please apply in tiny handwriting to the Crinkley Bottom Audio-Video Hi-Fi Repair Company, with brief history of your hand. Rubbing appreciated. Box 22.

Secretaries! Save energy during those really boring phone calls with the mega-ingenious Labour-Saving Notebook – every page pre-doodled with its own scribble, squiggle, or stick-man. Two pre-gnawed pen-tops with every order, PLUS! free rude-word speller check for companies dealing with the Great House. Layz-E-Gitz of Crinkley Bottom, Ltd. Box 32.

Why does it always get late around 11 p.m.?
Why do they keep putting pips in apples when nobody ever eats them?
Why isn't there a patron saint of patron saints?
Why does no one ever buy any of those trolleys you see in supermarkets?
Why do they build rubbish dumps under flocks of seagulls?
What colour is electricity?
Why are proof-readers so intanettive?
Why do hand-driers always cut out just before your hands are properly dry?
Why does Norway enter the Eurovision Song Contest?
Why does it never stop at one measle?
Why is *'Allo 'Allo* so popular?
The Crinkley Bottom Rhetorical Society would appreciate further questions to debate at its third inaugural conference. No SAEs – we can't provide answers, can we, you idiot ! Box 77.

Overprotected heir seeks puberty lessons. Quick! Box 55.

Amnesia victim (blonde, 5ft 2in, bi-lingual), found wandering unclothed in Tenderpart Court during the early hours of 9 January with jellyfish, tonsillitis and fresh tattoo, seeks explanation. Box 36.

Global warming: owing to the expected melting of the South Pole, foster parents will soon be required for homeless penguins. Previous experience is not necessary, although linoleum floors, large freezer unit, impeckable neighbours are a must. Please act now. Write, detailing the benefits you can offer, to the Penguin Homes of Crinkley Bottom Society, Box 366. The Society is also anxious to hear from villagers willing to accommodate polar bears on a temporary basis before permanent re-instatement in Skegness. No Eskimos, please.

Interconnective spiral flange and rearwinding blank scutcheon operatives required. Mk 2 equipment, plinker provided. No grutch bag necessary. Please state number of moles. Box 6½.

Bored orthodontist's wife seeks unusual things to do with dental floss. Box 8.

Unique Diagnoses (Crinkley Bottom), Inc. proudly announces a BREAKTHROUGH in diagnostic research. As an offshoot from recent advances in genetic fingerprinting techniques, our scientists are now able to detect minute but vital vitamin deficiencies from the body detritus, or 'fluff', which gathers naturally in the navel. This method is PRECISE, PAINLESS and PROMPT. Simply send us a sample, stating time, place and method of removal. Please do not bathe for fifteen days prior. We regret samples must be returned. Box 24.

For the connoisseur: authentic street plan of Crinkley Bottom as it appeared 100 years ago, in the 1790s. Gets you lost faster, more hopelessly, and for twice as long – ideal for minicab drivers. £15. Speedee-Con (Crinkley Bottom), Ltd. Box 666.

Researcher seeks further evidence of psychic experiences with baked beans. Box 57.

MARITAL SUSPICIONS? Worried you might be married? Suspect you've got a spouse? Find out for sure through our confidential marriage testing service. Just send us a sample of the possible partner, together with grounds for your suspicions. We will rush you the test results free and in absolute confidence within a week. Banish that nagging doubt now. Contact: The Charitable Trust for Better Marital Understanding. Box 40.

YOUR HELP NEEDED. Between 1 and 1.30 a.m. last Wednesday, Comet Aries passed equidistant between the Earth and the Moon, creating a unique arrangement of heavenly bodies and an unprecedented disturbance in the electromagnetic field over Crinkleyshire. The Crinkley Bottom Association for Para-Astrological and Spatial Research would like to hear from villagers who noticed strange atmospherical effects or met a tall dark stranger during this period. Box 4.

Lost your hoofer-doofer? Don't move ! Our hi-tech remote-control units operate all known GB and foreign TV sets. Just £19.99, with free 15-foot carrying case. Speedee-Con (Crinkley Bottom) Ltd. Box 666.

Our quick, simple and effective device will save you time cleaning your windows – PERMANENTLY! Good throwing arm required. Crinkley Bottom Brick Co. Box 82.

WHO'S A CLEVER BOY, THEN? Let us teach your parrot to talk properly. Eliminate embarrassment when visitors call. Feel superior at pet shows. £70 + VAT per term for day-birds. (Extracurricular courses in avian etiquette and deportment available for the right parrot.) Please write, enclosing photo, disposition, interests, uniform size, and character reference to: Improva Pet, Ltd. Box 31. STOP PRESS: Vacancies will shortly be available

---

Cure bedwetting permanently – sleep on the floor.

Help the Aged – loosen sauce bottle tops.

Prevent puppies scratching your best furniture – cut their legs off.

Avoid Acne – take the A102 through 'Ounslow.

Stop tits pecking through your milk bottle tops – put bricks on them.

With these tips, and others, the Herbert Society is providing essential advice to herberts throughout Crinkley Bottom. We're doing our best. But, with the number of herberts in Crinkley Bottom quadrupling each year, increasingly our best is not enough. We need more help – your help. So please, help a herbert today. Send whatever tips you can spare: no matter how small the Herbert Society welcomes them all. Box 14.

in our Crinkleyshire-famous Canine Finishing Classes. Interested owners should submit their hound's application for inclusion NOW! Strictly no Rottweilers.

Seasonal watches for hibernating pets. Radio or cuckoo alarm. One size, fits all paws. Improva Pet, Ltd. Box 31.

Wake up to the environment! Specially designed by the Crinkley Bottom Noise Abatement Society, our sound-free alarm clock doesn't ring – it flashes! Absolutely useless, but only £5.99. (Nominated for a No Bell prize.) Box 95.

Don't burn up! Buy a new ozone hole. Choice of sizes, colours, tog-ratings. Hundreds in stock. Nifty Ideas of Crinkley Bottom, Plc. Box 39.

Too busy for weekend picnics? The Instant Post-Picnic Hamper saves you hours. Chicken-leg bone, apple core, sandwich crusts, greasy forks, dirty plates and a mutilated plastic spoon all authentically jumbled up between crumbs, cling-film and a half-dead wasp in a genuine cowpat-stained hamper. Just pop it in the car, drive out to a pleasant country lane, and empty it all over the verge. Practically indistinguishable from the real thing. £50 or your money back. Layz-E-Gitz of Crinkley Bottom, Ltd. Box 32.

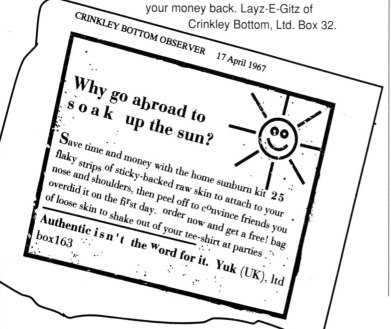

CRINKLEY BOTTOM OBSERVER   17 April 1967

Why go abroad to soak up the sun?

Save time and money with the home sunburn kit 25 flaky strips of sticky-backed raw skin to attach to your nose and shoulders, then peel off to convince friends you overdid it on the first day. order now and get a free! bag of loose skin to shake out of your tee-shirt at parties

Authentic isn't the word for it. Yuk (UK), ltd
box163

I HAVE FOUND THE MEANING OF LIFE! Would the person who lost it please contact me, and kindly explain why it had been left wrapped in newspapers under the back seat of a number 29 bus to Dangley End. Box 1.

Save £££s on home improvements! Get the genuine feel of expensive replacement windows for less than half the price with our incredible double-glazed spectacles. No fitting, no mess, no kidding! Speedee-Con (Crinkley Bottom), Ltd. Box 666.

Has your conventional toothbrush got you looking down in the mouth? Feeling too long in the tooth for all that scrubbing and swilling? KERPOW! Give old dental cleaning techniques the brush-off with the ultra-efficient Sonic Toothbrush from Crinkley Bottom. No toothpaste required! The Sonic Toothbrush simply blasts away plaque and bacteria with a single safe impulse of high-intensity sound, leaving your teeth frighteningly white and your mouth fresher than a walk in Firker's Wood. Special pre-introductory offer! Just complete the following sentence in an apt and amusing manner, using no more than fifteen words, and you could receive the revolutionary Sonic Toothbrush absolutely free! *'I'd like to use the Sonic Toothbrush in my gob, because ... '* Entries should be sent to Speedee-Con (Crinkley Bottom) Ltd. before the closing date for entries. Box 666.

Local publication has vacancy for clairvoyant. Box number will be known to suitable applicants.

Mums! Carry your baby the way nature intended with the amazing new Kangaroo Pouch. The very latest in infant mobility, this entirely genuine pouch hangs from the shoulders on non-abrasive straps, accommodating baby against the familiar security of the abdomen in style, in safety – and in sight! Soft, absorbent kangaroo fur keeps baby quiet and content for up to three weeks at a time. Zip or velcro fastenings with optional feeder and wee tubes. Reusable collection bag free with first fifty orders. Send for free trial, stating tummy size, and average weekly output, to: The Crinkley Bottom Marsupial Product and Doggydins Co. Box 407.

Is your cat a catastrophe? Are you dogged by your Dobermann? Whatever your pet hate, we can smarten up the animal in your life. Go-faster stripes for your tortoise, hair dye for your hamster, a nose job for your parrot, or a nice loose cover for your snake – you name it, we can do it, cheaply, quickly – legally! Send details of your feathered, finned or four-legged friend's short comings to: Improva Pet, Ltd. Box 31. Free pot of goldfish paint with first order.

For Sale: average pair of gloves (8 fingers, left hand; 2 fingers, right). Suit short-tempered motorist. Will deliver. Box 82.

Compilers of *The Modern Crinkley Bottom Dictionary* are in need of single words to describe each of the following: the process of dialling on a push-button phone; a group of woodlice; the action of typing on a wordprocessor; and the lump of hair, soap and toenails found in the plug-hole of the typical Crinkley Bottom bath. Maximum 732 letters. No hyphens. Box 445.

It's here at last! Spaghetti Conditioner – no more tangled Italian meals. £6.99. Speedee-Con (Crinkley Bottom), Ltd. Box 666.

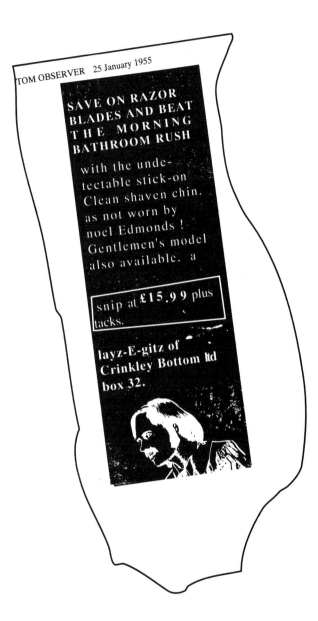

TOM OBSERVER   25 January 1955

SAVE ON RAZOR BLADES AND BEAT THE MORNING BATHROOM RUSH

with the unde-tectable stick-on Clean shaven chin. as not worn by noel Edmonds ! Gentlemen's model also available. a

snip at £15.99 plus tacks.

layz-E-gitz of Crinkley Bottom ltd box 32.

17. Scouting for Crinkley Bottomers

A guide on the scouts – advice to the intrepid, or a young lad's erotic fantasy? Simon Napkin, local scoutmaster and sheep-talc salesman, elucidates with the lowdown on the Crinkley Bottom Scout Troup.

Right, then. I suppose you already qualify as a potential Crinkley Bottom Scout. Anyone who's got this far through the book must have the sort of blind mindless tenacity we're looking for. So, what's it all about? Scouts: one word, six letters, and it's nothing to do with the language they speak in Liverpool. Got that?

So, about these Scouts. How do you become one? Some people would say the question should be, why do you become one? But that's one thing you have to put up with when you're a Crinkley Bottom Scout: jealousy.

Certain villagers – no names, no libel writs – just can't abide anyone having something they haven't got, like fine ideals, comradeship, and a twentieth-century haircut. Oh yes, they try to hide it, but you can tell: little things, you know, like parking their tractor on your patio table, spraying liquid manure through your letterbox, stuffing a cow's torso down your chimney – individually, subtle, easily overlooked incidents maybe; but taken as a whole you get the feeling that somebody's none too fond of you, particularly when it all happens in the same afternoon.

So, quality number one: thick skin. Got that? Right, then. Quality number two: endurance.

ENDURANCE: Yes, a Crinkley Bottom Scout's life isn't physically easy, either. At Summer Camp you'll be plucked out of bed at seven a.m., and taken on a comprehensive route march around every single bit of Crinkley Bottom. And you're not always finished then. At ten past seven, you might be marched off somewhere else.

SAFETY-CONSCIOUSNESS: Safe scouting does not mean practising your granny-knots, dressed in a rubber sheath. Although with the gooey bits of cattle splashing down the chimney, and half a dozen fathoms of cow muck in your

Harvest in Crinkley Bottom: village scouts often give a hand – an arm, an ear, a leg . . .

hallway, it may not be such a bad idea. But no, what we're aiming for here is preventative scouting. Don't look at me like that: I'm not asking you to spell it.

Preventative scouting involves taking the normal scouting situation, and thinking that little bit more sagaciously about it. Yes, I know that's an unfamiliar word, so I'll say it again: thinking. Pertinent examples of the art include persuading little old ladies they don't want to cross the road in the first place; drawing an imaginary straight line between the Liszt and Newt and the Great House, and not standing on it when opening hours are about to begin; and only offering to clean Terry Nutter's car after his German Shepherd/baby Brontosaurus cross has had its breakfast ... Terry's breakfast, Terry's brother's breakfast, Terry's father's breakfast, Terry's mother's breakfast ...

THE ABILITY TO FIND A MOSSY TREE: This is an old trick every Crinkley Bottom Scout should know. The way it works is like this: you're out in Wiggley Woggle Wood, say, tying important knots in things, tracking vital shrews, and generally being a scout when, all of a sudden, you become separated from the rest of the troop.

Even as the wave of sheer relief washes over you, you begin to realize that you're lost. Potential disaster! Quite apart from the risk of accidents, exposure and starvation, it's touch and go whether you'll get home in time for *Blue Peter*. You're alone, you're anxious, you're frightened. What do you do? All right, what do you do after that? Well, as I said, if you're a Crinkley Bottom Scout, you employ the fiendishly cunning mossy tree trick.

Use all your native Crinkley Bottom

scouting skills to track down a mossy tree. Then simply stand under it, and yell, 'Help! I'm lost under a mossy tree.' Ingenious, effective, and it saves a fortune on maps and compasses. Next!

TWO DRY STICKS: No point beating out the bird in the bush on this one. Anyone who becomes a scout in Crinkley Bottom will at some stage be called upon to perform, shall we say, unnatural acts? No, we won't; we'll grasp the gift horse by the horns, and say you're going to have to ... smile. There! the cat's out of the china shop. Come on, now; I know it's abhorrent and weird and as a typical modern yoof, you think mirth is something Jesus got off the wise men, but when you're a scout you really have to be brave and face up to smiling.

Education: Using just two dry sticks and a little lung power, a Crinkley Bottom scout is about to set his hair on fire.

See, being of service to his community is a scout's raison d'être, and a concomitant part of that is raison d'lips. This is hard enough to accomplish in a normal town or village: but in Crinkley Bottom, where being of service seems to mean helping villagers force a dripping carcass down one of your domestic orifices, or directing a twenty-ton agricultural vehicle on to your garden furniture, it's a bitch.

So you're going to need all the willpower and self-control you can shake your woggle at. And a couple of dry sticks will come in handy, too. Having helpfully rubbed them together to start a fire under – sorry, for – a local villager, you can wedge them in your mouth to stop your back teeth disintegrating while you try to smile at him.

LOCKSMITH SKILLS: Bob-a-Job Week is when we scouts call on Crinkley Bottom villagers hoping to receive generous sums of money in return for the little jobs we carry out for them. Car washing, gardening and window cleaning present no problem for us, but we desperately need someone to deal with the epidemic of jammed front-door locks we inexplicably seem to encounter at this time of year.

ANATOMY: Sorry to bring up such a delicate subject as the anatomy, but even in Crinkley Bottom you're going to need one. Preferably not a large one, because this is the only village in Britain where you need planning permission for a bust enlargement. The scout hut's a shade cramped, too: at the moment, we're saving up for paint to cover the 'Average Contents 43' notice on its side.

But lack of size isn't everything, and a scout here also needs the physical resilience to withstand local nature red in false tooth and claw. If you were to pin me down – and I'm free most Friday nights – I would say the ideal Crinkley Bottom Scout should be short, round-shouldered, bottom-heavy, small-headed, squeaky-voiced,

immature enough not to be distracted by girls, and ugly enough not to distract them.

Yes, yes, I know this is a tall order for just one person, but look on the bright side: if Noel Edmonds can manage it, so can you.

BEING PREPARED: A scout in Crinkley Bottom must always be prepared. He must be prepared to have his knees giggled at, his hat knocked off, his woggle flicked up his nose, his shorts peeked up, his tent combine-harvested, his camp fire declared a disaster area, his sleeping bag mistaken for a purse from the Great House, and his penknife borrowed to prise the *Crinkley Bottom Observer*'s editor off his barstool in the Liszt and Newt.

COMPETITIVENESS: Many's the aspiring Crinkley Bottom Scout who's nose-dived at this

It's suprising who develops a taste for Scouts

74

hurdle. I remember poor Podgy Squitters who was so uncompetitive he dropped out of long bus queues. This rarely proved a problem in Crinkley Bottom, because we don't have any long buses.

None the less, competitiveness is a crucial part of the Crinkley Bottom Scout's make-up – not that we wear ... well, only that once at Summer Camp, and ... Anyway, competitiveness leads to increased effort; increased effort leads to improved performance; and improved performance leads to – and this is what it's all about, lads – badges!

The world would be a far finer place if we all had badges. Think how the nation's IQ would rise if TV viewers could earn their 'I Sat Through Panorama Without Nodding Off' badge. How many trains would be late if train drivers were in the running for an 'I Got There Without Slowing to a Crawl and Kangarooing Along for Miles for No Apparent Reason' badge? And how much less

smelly the countryside would be if refuse collectors had the chance to gain their 'I Carried a Bin Full of Cans Down a Drive Without Dropping One' badge.

Sad to say, the Crinkley Bottom Scout Troop's badge tally lately amounts to just one Knot Tying badge, awarded when the toilet tent blew away at Summer Camp, and half a dozen Survival badges, four of which were awarded posthumously.

The eighties scouts had a little more success. Pigmy Hislop, for one. Only one thing prevented him winning his Self-sufficiency badge: he couldn't find anyone to help him pin it on. Dick O'Crumbs, the local baker, had more luck in '86. His Culinary badge for 'Cooking Beans Over a Camp Fire' brought great rejoicing in the Troop, although Beans's mum wasn't too pleased about it. And young Nobby Magnusson's 1985 Tracking badge is to go on show in the scout hut, just as

Summer camp, 1991: Crinkley Bottom Scouts decide they're 3.68 miles south-west of Nickeredgs-on-Vue, shortly before being arrested by Chilean military police.

soon as he can find it. The scout hut, that is. Tiddler Tarbuck attained an Orienteering badge in 1983, and you can still see the holes in his forehead where he pinned it on. But that's probably the only Orienteering badge we're ever likely to get if the majority of our old scouts is any guide.

Twiggy Rushton – remember him? – the only lad capable of getting lost in a phone box. Then there was Lord Nose's son Beaky, who couldn't go for more than five minutes on an exercise bike without stopping to ask the way. And the lack of orienteering ability demonstrated by Scout Edmonds is renowned throughout Crinkley Bottom. Unable to locate his mid–rearward section with both hands as a lad, his sense of misdirection has since blossomed so that now he can't even find his way to lending anyone a fiver.

THE PIONEERING SPIRIT: Trudging for miles to fetch water in an old pail, washing laundry on the rocks beside the River Crinkle,

sleeping woggle-deep in rodents and insects, breakfasting off scavenged scraps and berries, going for weeks without a bath, digging primitive toilets, spending hours gathering wood to cook a rude evening meal: these are the hardships facing the scout in Crinkley Bottom. And when he leaves home for Summer Camp, things can get even worse.

So there you have it: the qualities and skills, temperament and standards needed to become a Crinkley Bottom Scout. Onerous and exacting maybe, but if you feel you can live up to them, pop in to our scout hut some time and introduce yourself to the Troop. I'm sure we'll both be pleased to meet you. There, finished at last. Now, that's £3.50 an hour I owe Edmonds for the typewriter ... I wonder if Fanny Smalls does a 32p postal order?

18. Political Animals

The head of Crinkley Bottom Council has a great cure for insomnia: he goes to work. It may not be as convenient as two sleeping tablets, but it's certainly not addictive. Only last week, a motion accusing Councillors of being apathetic towards attendance was defeated by one vote to nil. And that was only because one Councillor voted twice.

They're an honest bunch, Crinkley Bottom Councillors – provided you don't take their criminal records into account – and easily wounded by criticism. So concerned were they over an allegation that members were being profligate with tax payers' money recently, they called an extraordinary general meeting and immediately flew out to Grand Canary to discuss it.

The Council represents all five main political viewpoints in the village: Pros, Antis, Don't Knows, Don't Cares, and Get Out of Here, You Lying Twerps. Its leader swept to power on a landslide, after ten years' futile electioneering, when he changed his name from Herbert Bullsitter to Herbert Bullsitter-X. His right-hand man, Penelope Utter-Twaddle, is a banana weaver from Dangley End, Monk's Bottom, Naffall-to-Sea, and Crinkleton. (She was born on a train.)

The Council's upper echelon is completed by Walter Whopper, a careful fish polisher; Phyllis Stein, the hydraulic poet; Gordon Bennett-Moore-Guff, Crinkley Bottom's own puncture repair kit repairman; and eighty-nine-year-old

Food for thought: will Penelope Utter-Twaddle get planning permission for another plate of biscuits?

Lord Nose, who's hoping to become a High Court judge when he dies.

Muriel Constant-Wittering handles Mister Bullsitter's private functions, for which she's given her own line-prop and a generous rubber-gloves allowance. She's a mother of two, although the more sceptical council members suspect she's much older than that.

Prominent among the minor officials are Phil E. Buster, grease investigator and tea-money fan; Anna Partridge, sheep rubber; the enigmatic I.B. Fuddled, OR, sock advisor; and Ida Knoe, who believes the Tower of Pisa is perpendicular and the rest of the world is leaning at an angle of seventy-nine point six degrees.

Acting individually, with others, or sometimes as all eight quarters of a more than complete whole, these innumerable few have been responsible for some of the finest biscuit selections the world has ever seen. This is local government at its crunchiest. Democracy? – these people don't mind whose sponge fingers they eat.

Meetings are bi-weekly once a month in the first-class section of the village hall (clean window; optional floor): they feature big debates, small debates, long debates, short debates, fast debates, slow debates, solo debates, and mass discussions. The village hall lends itself to such meetings – which is lucky, because the caretaker certainly wouldn't lend it. Opposite the wall where the voting booths are supposed to be stand the voting booths: twelve individual, narrow boxes, each lit by a lonely bulb, and ingeniously curtained off with a curtain. When a vote is called, Councillors enter a booth, draw the curtain, and place a cross on the ballot paper. If it's a secret vote, they take the light bulb out.

The end of the hall – something which has more support than all the local parties – is taken up by a misspelt dais. Here it was that legendary ex-Council Chief Executive and amnesiac Gerald Dronin-Burke delivered both his maiden speeches. Either side of the dais, two chairs are roughly laid out. They're Ronnie and Reggie Chair, the professional defendants, taking a well-earned throatbreak from their continuous loop of village pubs.

In the main body of the hall, the caretaker and his mate spend the day setting out seats for the public. They're old and rickety, with mouldy bottoms, rotten arms and missing legs – and the seats aren't much better. But it is on these seats that villagers with a concern for local issues, and no concern for life and limb, sit. Often for minutes at a time. It tends to be the same group, headed by Nobby Magnusson, the railway-porter spotter, and bottomed by Snooty Somerville, perennial débutante and Sellotape sniffer. Its midriff encompasses the semi-colon collector Pimply O'Connor, who first propounded the eternal truth that everything in Crinkley Bottom is near everything else; Jez Oik, the man who puts the crass in democracy; Tiddler Tarbuck, widely acknowledged to be three points short of an agenda; and the multi-pocketed Squinty Travis, rice artist and international cushion planner.

And who could discuss politics in Crinkley Bottom without mentioning Sir Alistair Noisy-Trumper, the distinguished villager who once completed a crossword clue. Nobody keeps Sir Alistair away from Council meetings. He manages it very well all by himself.

It's said the most bored man in Crinkley Bottom must be the local mind reader. If so, villagers attending Council meetings run him a pretty close second. So, what attracts them? What, actually, does the Crinkley Bottom Council do? Curiously enough, this is the very question Tubs Wogan posed in the Winking Nun the night he went missing. The answer to it is not simple. It's just about the only thing in Crinkley Bottom that isn't.

What's plain for all to see is the peerless role Council teabreaks play in promoting village trade: Crinkley Bottom's biscuit factory employees are working their rich tea fingers to the bone; fig roll manufacturers are constantly on the go; and the local baker's working his ginger nuts off.

The gathering of local statistics is a less obvious Council duty. Their latest extensive

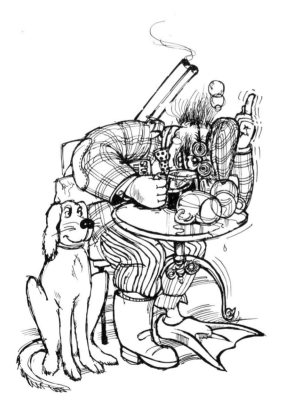

Sir Alistair Noisy-Trumper: campaigner for the extension of round-the-clock pud opening hours

survey, carried out in the chocolate chip cookie section of the local Pea Shoppe, had to be abandoned when four villagers became trapped in the clipboard, but not before it revealed that Mrs Bulstrode has never been older than she is today.

Where taxation is concerned, the Council's approach is always admirably determined. In 1989, when lesser Councils quailed beneath the wave of poll tax revolts, Crinkley Bottom Council remained steadfast, set an unequivocal rate, and told villagers they had one year to pay it. Most chose the year 2038.

In keeping with its motto, Liberté-Egalité-Naïveté, the Council has its considerate side, too. Word has it they've agreed to grant the Liszt and Newt's latest application for an extension to its opening hours – just as soon as they can find a twenty-fifth hour in the day.

But there are also negative aspects to the Councillors' work. To them fell the task of cancelling the village's Miss Crinkley Bottom Contest, when it became painfully clear that nobody did.

1987 saw their much questioned decision to recall all village litterbins, following revelations that people were just throwing their rubbish in them. On much the same principle, the local WC was withdrawn from service a year later. And in 1990, Crinkley Bottom Prison was closed after an investigation revealed it contained nothing but a load of crooks (grounds, incidentally, which nearly led to the Council having to close itself down).

The man who must take ultimate responsibility for these decisions is Village Mayor Pointy Finnegan. Yet, at Council meetings when controversial issues are raised, he never argues, never interrupts, never blusters, never shouts, never hurls abuse – he never turns up, in fact.

Not for nothing is Pointy known as the Halley's Comet of village politics. In this, he is following in a long line of Crinkley Bottom Mayors, all of whom had so little experience of local government they thought a by-law was some kind of overthrow rule in cricket.

Mayors notwithstanding, though, Council members do try to show an interest in what goes on during their meetings. Walter Whopper is always most concerned to see the custard creams maintain their pre-eminent position on the biscuit trolley. Penelope Utter-Twaddle is waging a personal campaign for improved local Garibaldi care. And I.B. Fuddled, OR, makes no secret of his worryingly militant belief that Council funding should be increased in the field of Bath Oliver acquisition.

Attempts are also in hand to make the Council more village-friendly. Council Leader's Question Time, where locals can come and put their questions to Herbert Bullsitter, has been introduced on Tuesday and Thursday evenings. It was going to be called Council Leader's Answer Time, but accuracy prevailed.

Still more adventurous was the announcement that the Council was to fund a series of television advertisements for itself on CBS, a move which left villagers gasping in amazement until they realized it stood for Crinkley Bottom Satellite. Experienced Bottomists will know that this isn't the first time Councillors have dallied with the modern media. Penelope Utter-Twaddle's party political broadcast on CBTV last year elicited an instant and highly favourable response. It came from Jenny-Jenny Nutter (aged three and a half), thanking the station for bringing back *Jackanory*.

Undeniably, Crinkley Bottom politics have come a long way since their feudal beginnings, when dictatorial lords spent the day surfing, with real serfs, and villagers at election time were told it was their Count that votes. Yes, many of us still remember the eighties. But, to be frank, average public attendances of six, and a quarter-column write-up on the cartoon page of the *Crinkley Bottom Sunday Observer* every Wednesday, is not what we've come to expect from a Council which is supposed to be leading us bravely into the present day.

So, Herbert Bullsitter has dug out the Council agenda for next year (1873, Crinkley Bottom Time). Having peeled off the jammy dodger, he's given it to me, hoping that publication of the questions the Council are to address will attract a wider, more astute audience to their meetings. And he could be right: a couple of top Dangley End psychiatrists have already booked season tickets.

JANUARY

How do ants tell one another apart?
How come people who wear glasses always seem to have poor eyesight?
What did people talk about before words were invented?
Why can't you poke about in your eye without opening your mouth?

FEBRUARY

How come your body's got two of everything except the things you really want two of?
Does God really like hymns?

When will Parliament impose the death penalty for bagpiping?

MARCH

If female frogs lay 3,000 eggs an hour, why does it take waitresses so long to lay a table?
What's the point of eyebrows?
Why do we always have Bank Holidays when the roads are so busy?

APRIL

Why won't parrots look you straight in the eye?
Where did Stone Age man get his fillings replaced?
What's so important that sparrows have to get up so early?

MAY

If the sun turns people brown, why does it turn your settee white?
Why does it seem eminently sensible to keep the key to the lock you changed eight years ago?
Why do goldfish always seem to know what you're thinking about?

JUNE

What do sheep see in Welsh farmers?
If light travels at 186,000 miles per second, why don't you hear a sonic boom every time you turn a torch on?

How come all the people who write to agony columns have problems?

JULY

How do hedgehogs manage to mate without stabbing themselves to death?
Why do floorboards only creak after midnight?
If the universe is continually expanding, how come your living-room rug still reaches the sideboard?
Why can't you buy a bottle of shampoo without 25 per cent extra in it?

AUGUST

Why can't chameleons just choose one colour and stick to it?
Why do mice eat so much, but never get any bigger?
Why don't people shrink after a hot bath?

SEPTEMBER

Why do skulls always look so cheerful?
What colour does litmus paper turn litmus paper?
If it takes three weeks to learn to ride, how did anyone ever get around to inventing the bicycle?

OCTOBER

Why is a town on the north-west coast of England called Southport?
Why's there always an orange-juice stain on page

63 of your library book?
Do spiders scream when they see a big hairy human being in the bath?
Why do you never see it raining in an oil painting?
If Beethoven was so brilliant, how come he couldn't pronounce his name properly?

NOVEMBER

Why do stately home owners think they can attract more visitors by letting lions loose in their grounds?
Why is it mechanically impossible for a car to break down less than one mile away from a telephone box?
Why can't you blow your nose without looking in your handkerchief afterwards?
Where does chronic masochism end, and supporting Crinkley Bottom Wonderers begin?

DECEMBER

Why don't Eskimos move somewhere warmer?
Why does the phone never ring when you're bored?
Do cows know more than they're letting on?
Why's it thought necessary to nail down the coffin-lids on dead people?
Whose turn is it to embezzle Council funds for next year's supply of arrowroot biscuits, lemon puffs, fig rolls, Bath Olivers, chocolate fingers, Wagon Wheels, Hobnobs, marshmallows, Rich Tea fingers, Maryland cookies, Garibaldis, Custard Creams, Chocolate Clubs, Wholemeal Digestives, Brandy Snaps, Gipsy Creams, Kit Kats, tartan shortbreads, teatime assorteds, Abbey Crunches, caramel wafers, morning coffees, Jaffa Cakes ...?

19. Festive Frolics

For a village that's been all at sea since its foundation, Crinkley Bottom boasts astonishingly few mariners. No one really knows why. It can't be that the inhabitants prefer to stay in the village. Maybe they have a congenital fear of water, like the Scotch drinkers in the Liszt and Newt. Whatever the reason, one man defied the trend back in 1892: Captain Horatio Noseblower.

Setting sail from Naffall Harbour, Noseblower was soon braving the rigours and perils of the Seven Seas – which came as a bit of a shock, as he'd only intended going to Frinton.

It rapidly became clear that Noseblower was no mean seafarer. Some went so far as to say he was no seafarer at all. And so, with the scent of salt in his nostrils and the smell of herrings in his socks, young Noseblower joined the fearless British Navy. As a gangplank.

There were a few setbacks at first: the ship's cat got promoted over him; and, on receiving orders to make two pirates walk the plank, he tied six feet of rope to a floorboard, and told them to drag it around the deck for an hour. None the less, Noseblower's stout sea-loving heart shone through (it wasn't hard – his jacket was threadbare), and at the age of eighteen, he was awarded his own parrot. All he needed now was a shoulder to put it on.

From this moment on, for Noseblower, there was no looking back – he'd put a crick in his neck watching the parrot. Within years, the Navy not only gave him his own ship, but also said he could keep the bottle it came in.

As a captain commanding HMS *Anon*,

1901 found Noseblower striking fear into the black hearts of every brigand and ne'er-do-well that ever sailed the Crinkleyshire coast. But his navigational skills soon improved, and in 1903 his courageous crossing of the Atlantic Ocean would have been a world first for Crinkley Bottom but for one thing. He never attempted it.

In conflict at sea, no matter how bloody the battle, Noseblower was never armed with anything more lethal than his trusty three-inch dagger. It was foolhardiness; it was bravado; but it was all he could carry up to the crow's nest with him.

A bold leader, indeed. And yet a caring one: he made sure every man aboard ship had his own rum ration. And he had theirs.

In his day (generally acknowledged to be 3 June 1889), Noseblower brought glory and honour to Crinkley Bottom. And now, with a lifetime's supply of experience and parrot droppings behind him, Captain Horatio Noseblower, RTG (Retired, Thank God) picks up his telescope once more, turns his unpatched eye to that self-same village, and navigates us through a wintry wonderland of village Christmas traditions...

Ahoy, there, Edmonds! Call that a beard? I've seen more hairs on a potty. Gather round now, me hearties! I've a tale to tell, and half a mind to tell it. You hear them, don't you, lads, all over the empire – the sort of buffoons who keep losing their glasses and grumbling about five-pee pieces: 'Christmas isn't what it used to be,' they bluster. 'No magic these days, no character, no excitement, bally-all goodwill. Bally tradition's gone out of the thing, that's the trouble.'

What a load of old shiny balls! Come down to Crinkley Bottom, that's what I say to them, shipmates! Crinkley Bottom Christmases are as stuffedful of traditions as they've always been. You can't stumble down the street without being kept on your feet by one. Big traditions, little traditions, old traditions, new traditions, traditions behind the filing cabinet, traditions with batteries not included, traditions in brown bottles, traditions in green bottles, traditions in specimen bottles ... There are more blasted traditions in Crinkley Bottom today than you can shake a Scotsman's Christmas stocking at, lads. Thing is, the bally old fusters who complain can't be bothered to put down their *Witchburners' Weekly* and bally well look for them. Well, I've bally well looked for them. And here they bally well are!

BEING SICK UNDER THE CHRISTMAS TREE

This is a grand old Crinkley Bottom Christmas tradition – colourful, warm, full of surprises – redolent with childhood memories of menfolk returning from the hostelry, gathering round the Christmas tree, and emptying what seemed to be the entire contents of their alimentary canals around its trunk.

Aye, the memory plays tricks, shipmates, and it was in all likelihood just the undigested bits of the stomach, plus some slime from the upper duodenum. Even so, what generosity, eh, lads? What a spontaneous outpouring of community spirit! What guts! And isn't it heart-warming to know that with the sort of tum-churning Crinkley Bottom TV programmes served up for us at Christmas, this tradition will be around in the village for a long, long time to come.

TURNING OFF NOEL EDMONDS

This is a tradition the whole village can join in and enjoy. But, like most traditions, it goes deeper than that.

By broadcasting Noel Edmonds at Christmas, CBTV is doing its bit to promote family life. In effect, it's saying to you, Go on, shipmate – turn the telly off, make your own entertainment, relearn the art of conversation, get to know the bally old family again. It's a revolutionary approach to broadcasting, and one likely to bring about a finer quality of life at home. And egad! We could all do with that in Crinkley Bottom.

Once they've learned to use these old communication skills, villagers find it needn't just stop at Christmas. They'll be able to turn off Noel Edmonds any time – any hour, any day, anywhere. Just like 99 per cent of the rest of the population, in fact.

DESTROYING A RAIN FOREST

It's a great feeling: Christmas Day has finally arrived in Crinkley Bottom – the pressies are being oohed over, the ankle biters' eyes are so big and bright they're frightening the cat. Meanwhile, behind Aunty Edith – tearful and toothless on the settee – rises a paper plateau of discarded gift-wrapping, roughly the same size as a Jovian moon. All this, and it's only 3.33 in the morning. Great feeling, my lads.

With such an extravagant waste of the Earth's scarce wood pulp resources staring them in the face, some lubbers would be tempted to feel guilty. Not us Crinkley Bottomers, me hearties. We know that every crumpled sheet, every torn tissue, every crushed gift tag has gone towards reducing the scale of the world's appalling equatorial rain forest problem.

Between you and me and the parrot, shipmates: appalling equatorial rain forests have spread through our middle latitudes like the suppurating green blotches of some rampant tropical disease. Take it from an expert. They're gnarly, sticky, snaggly, sweaty, creaky, tangly, pongy, oxygeny, and thick with things that croak, creep, crap, snap, splash, squawk, sting, scuttle, screech, slither, buzz, plop, and go burr-up-durr-whee!-whoop-whoop.

It's enough to put you off your rum ration, lads. What a good thing our quaint Crinkley Bottom Christmas custom of wrapping pressies in poopdecksful of precious paper is keeping these bally forests in check – and not only in check, shipmates, but forcing them to retreat and, in some cases, actually disappear completely.

Aye, I'll grant you, certain ecological benefits derive from rain forests – like the insects, animals and plants required to maintain the food chain, and the oxygen essential for continued human survival on this planet. But, surely, lads, these are minor considerations compared to the jolly things we could do with the kilo-oodles of empty space left when the forests are cleared. We could build a nice new office block, or a reception centre for left-handed Nepalese dandruff sufferers. Or maybe even another multi-storey car park!

Whatever, the longer this fine old tradition of parcelling Crissy gifts survives, the sooner the threat from those bally old trees will be removed for good. And then we'll all be able to breathe more easily, eh, shipmates?

HEAD DUNKING

Christmas morning in Crinkley Bottom: hubbie gives his missus something she's always wanted –

no, lads, not that, not in Crinkley Bottom – and he finds the batteries aren't included. Unbuckle me swash! Never mind, though, he's sure he's seen a couple of HP180s lying around somewhere. Where was it now? ... Ah, yes! the bottom of that priceless vase on the mantelpiece.

A Crinkley Bottomer gets stuck in

Still befuddled from the village Christmas party, last September, hubbie rushes across, plunges his head in to check, and ... gets stuck. Doggone! he falls for it every year. And with doctors at Christmas about as easy to get hold of as a Romanian gymnast's buttock, he's probably going to be in there until Easter.

One consolation, though, lads: if he's planning any late-night village wassailing, at least he won't have to look at himself in the mirror next morning.

SLUICING THE DRIVEWAY

One of the more unpleasant aspects of Christmas in Crinkley Bottom is the prevalence of poor, cold, hungry folk roaming our streets in search of food and shelter. We know them better as the in-laws. Or words to that effect. And it's their job to make our Christmas as difficult as possible.

Crinkley Bottomers, therefore, make a tradition of avoiding them, shipmates. A bucket of iced water sloshed down the driveway every thirty minutes during peak visiting hours works a treat. Faint-hearted trippers are discouraged from venturing further; more reckless relations are put out of action permanently. It's rollicking stuff, me hearties. With traditions like this, you can actually look forward to getting a pair of slippers at Christmas!

BUYING PRESSIES

Come clean, lads: having to buy presents takes all the pleasure out of Christmas. Not in Crinkley Bottom it doesn't, me hearties! In Crinkley Bottom, we have a tradition of keeping all the presents we buy for ourselves. It's quite easy: we just remember not to give them to anyone else.

This often proves too complicated for some villagers, who find it helps to stick on a quaint gift tag bearing their own name in large capital letters. And if they're especially fond of themselves, they add a few kisses and wish themselves a Happy New Year, too. Aye, lads, all this tends to lessen the element of surprise on Christmas morning. But at least we're sure of receiving something a shade more exciting than socks and hankies and bally soap-on-a-rope.

NOT BUYING HOLLY

There are several things which have no place in the Crinkley Bottom Christmas: diets, sustained movement, bally soap-on-a-rope, seven o'clock in the morning, and sobriety. But none is more untenable than the customary twee sprig of holly. What this turgid, green, shrivelled-up excuse for foliage has to do with the festive season is a mystery on a par with the *Marie Celeste* and Ian MacCaskill's accent. Yet, every year without fail, outwardly sane lubbers don orange anoraks and woolly hats and tear themselves to shreds in search of the stuff. Others find shopping at the supermarket too competitive, and risk a bottyful of leadshot by picking their own from a cheery old farmer's wood. Villagers here believe it's far safer to stay at home: light the fire, uncork some lunch, and leaf well alone. To put it bluntly, lads, in Crinkley Bottom, holly at Christmas is just for pricks.

THINKING OF THE OLD

There's nothing wrong with thinking of the old at Christmas. Many of us think of Joan Collins quite a lot. That's about all we can do. Aye, take it from me, shipmates, provided you're not eating at the time, you can think of the old as much as you like. But this is not a Christmas tradition exclusive to Crinkley Bottom. Lubbers from Dangley End think of the old at Christmas, too: they generally think of them caught petrified in their headlights half-way across a zebra crossing.

In Nether Scratching, they think of them as boring and bad-tempered. And Bumpkins Enders think of them as just a waste of space in the doctor's waiting-room. Odds bodkins, lads! What philistines.

In Crinkley Bottom we think old people are just like us. Only worse. As such, they deserve a little respect and consideration. So at Christmas we always pop round and offer to lend a hand with their festive preparations – join the hunt for their false teeth, for example, or help twist the top off their daily bottle of gin. And as it's a religious occasion, we also offer spiritual assistance, and show the old dears how to make out their wills. It's a warm and very human thing to do, lads, and we feel so much more comfortable knowing they've spelt our names right.

DISPOSING OF THE YOUNG

Being dragged from your hammock by your son and hair at half past three on a cold and frosty Christmas morning has to be the most persuasive argument yet for compulsory birth control or voluntary baldness.

Young 'uns are allergic to Christmas. There's something about the familiar dank odour of old tinsel and ageing Brussels sprouts that turns them into intolerable little monsters. As opposed to the barely tolerable little monsters they usually are. Their tiny eyes light up like rear foglamps. Their stubby fingers contort into tight claws. They become hyperactive. They can't sleep. They develop an insatiable desire to own things. If the latest bally multi-mongrel orange were found to produce these symptoms in rats, it'd be banned before you could say pith. But as it's only good old merry Crissy, everyone seems to think it's OK. Well, in Crinkley Bottom, lads, it's not.

Crinkley Bottomers believe ankle biters and Christmas should be kept as far apart as possible. And, as I know well, you can't get much further than Marrakesh. So we bundle them off, baggage freight, with half a dozen *Beano*s and a roller-skate, at the beginning of the Christmas hols, and arrange for them to be shipped back some time after May. Like October. If they refuse to comply, or attempt to alert the RSPCC, we simply lock them in the loft and go to Marrakesh ourselves.

Anyone worrying about the havoc their offspring will wreak while they're away, simply get a baby-sitter for the little darlings. It's a wrench at first, but in time they find it's the best swap they ever made.

GRAVY

Gravy is a traditional part of our village Crissy. While lesser lubbers use it to disguise the taste of their vegetables, in Crinkley Bottom gravy has far more rewarding uses. Cold, shivery village carol singers are just dying for a drop.

For best results, we carry a cauldronful to an upstairs window, and wait for the little blighters to descend on us like unfed sharks.

A Crinkley Bottomer enforces his no-wailing ban

This can occur any evening from about Bonfire Night onwards. The best time to catch them is after they've started singing and before they've rung the doorbell: this gives us roughly two point two six seconds. So speed is essential.

Tipping the cauldron smoothly and often, we ensure the gravy flows evenly over the wailers below. The important thing is to hang on to the cauldron when it's empty: this way, if any of the herberts manages to evade his gravy shampoo, we've got something hard and lethal to throw at him afterwards.

Using up the festive gravy in this fashion does leave the question of what to do with our vegetables at Christmas dinner. This might cause problems in other parts of the country, but in Crinkley Bottom the answer's simple, me hearties: we just don't invite them.

TAKING

Speaking as a Crinkley Bottomer of long standing – in bally supermarket queues, butchers' queues, off-licence queues – there's far too much giving at Christmas and not enough taking. Which is why villagers here add a little cheer to the festive season with a spot of traditional Crinkley Bottom taking – taking liberties with our boss's secretary, for instance, taking a taxi to the pub, taking our wives for granted, taking extra days off work, and taking our mother-in-laws to a top London restaurant. And leaving them there. What a game, lads! And talking of games, me hearties, that reminds me ...

GAMES

It's Christmas evening in Crinkley Bottom: the young 'uns' presents have all been broken ... by Dad, the instant camera's out of film, Seb and Wayne are out hiring a container lorry to take back the empties, CBTV's so boring the Toby jug on the set's started snoring, the Crissy pud's been eaten, the Brussels sprouts have been drunk, and the turkey's finally gone – taking Father-in-law with her.

It's bally yawnful. So what do villagers do to liven things up? No, we don't wire up Uncle Bill's hearing-aid to the Christmas tree lights: we turn to one of our traditional old village games. Then, when we remember our traditional old village games are about as exciting as watching snakes slough, we turn to one of our traditional new village games. And what a lot there are to choose from: Hitting the Robin with a Mince Pie, Hiding the Holly in Grandpa's Slipper, Bobbing for Drowned Kittens.

My own festive favourites include Hunt the Christmas Spirit, Pass the Street Collector, Bank Manager's Bluff, Spot the Salmonella Victim, Spin the Drunkard, and the chuckle-packed Throw the Yule Log Through the Neighbours' Greenhouse Window, and Pin the Blame on the Kids. No game, though, can hold a Christmas candle to our popular New Year pursuit of First Footing, where villagers race to wedge the first foot up the rent collector's posterior.

CARD GAMES

Card games, too, provide much harmless traditional entertainment in Crinkley Bottom at Christmas. But to get the most out of them, shipmates, you've got to play them right. And playing them right in Crinkley Bottom means parking outside the house of someone you once met three years ago in the Pea Shoppe, waiting until 11.59, then dashing out to slot a Crissy card through their letter box, thus leaving him with absolutely no chance of sending you one in return before the midnight deadline. Like the barmaid of the Liszt and Newt, it gives you a really warm festive feeling, lads.

TEMPORARY OBLIVION

Temporary oblivion is a tempting prospect in Crinkley Bottom at Christmas time – and most other times of the year, as far as I'm concerned, lads. But how to achieve it, eh?

A drunken stupor entered into on or around October the thirteenth, and maintained until the FA Cup Final, can be satisfying. And, with luck, you'll even miss the New Year Scottish TV special. But it's expensive, lads, and difficult to get into the pub for a top-up on Christmas Eve. Mary and Joseph had problems 2,000 years ago, and the situation's not much better today.

So Crinkley Bottomers turned to the animal kingdom – no, lads, not France – and saw that after 17,000 years of evolution, the village-common-or-garden hedgehog, hamster, and tortoise have all got Crissy down to a fine art – they spend it in hibernation.

Thus, come the first flurry of festive trailers on the box, many villagers traditionally enter a deep and dreamless sleep. Unlike the rest of us, though, they've developed an ability to sustain this enviable state until the first cuckoo of spring comes knocking at the door with his new double-glazing catalogue.

The villager in Christmas hibernation needs neither food nor alcohol to survive; he just takes a pot noodle and a drop of the local beer every now and again. But this sort of skill is not acquired overnight, shipmates, especially when you're a Crinkley Bottomer.

The villager practises at first by rubbing linseed oil into his chest, and hiding in the wardrobe till teatime. This mastered, he wraps himself in an old *Crinkley Bottom Observer*, and asks a parent or elder brother to lock him in the garden shed for a month. If this works, he goes on to spend Crissy in a state of complete mental and physical inactivity. If it doesn't work, he resumes life as a typical Crinkley Bottom villager. The traditional game for friends and family, meanwhile, lads, is trying to tell the difference.

20. Famous Last Words

Crinkley Bottom is a suppository of notable features – many of them on Daph Titted's face – but none more famous than that classic example of local verve and energy, the village cemetery. So strong is interest in this venue that all villagers pay the place at least one visit. Sooner or later.

Crinkley Bottom's cemetery also proves a compulsive attraction for tourists, who are drawn there partly to seek out somewhere with more life than the village night club, partly to view the spot where a particularly slothful villager apparently came back to life thirty-two years after rigor mortis was thought to have set in, partly to visit Tubs Wogan's tomb – which, although 180 years old, still has more body in it than the local beer – but mainly to read for themselves Crinkley Bottom's legendary Inscribed Gravestones.

Rising like a battered bottom denture from the mist along the River Crinkle, these ancient miniliths baffle historians throughout the world and beyond. How, they ask, did the supposedly simple and isolated Crinkley Bottom community of the eighteenth century discover words? Where did they learn to spell them? And why has that nollidge pratickly disappeared today? Who can say? What we can do is marvel at the words, both old and new, engraved on those gravestones – epitaphs which, according to local custom, record faithfully

the final utterances of the courageously bold, but strangely stupid occupants below ...

Don't worry; they couldn't hit an elephant at this dist— . . .

I know a short-cut through the safari park.

It's just a spot of heartburn.

Shout and warn everyone we're in an avalanche area.

According to my new Taiwanese watch, we've still got fifteen minutes before this bomb explo— . . .

Give me a match to find this petrol leak, would you?

The cars will stop when we step on the zebra crossing.

And if you look out of the starboard portholes, ladies and gentlemen, you'll see that we're about to enter the Bermuda Triangle.

I'll just ask that man with the scar where the best place is to deposit this thousand pounds in used notes.

I take thee, Bangkok Lil, to my lawful wedded wife.

We'll get a lovely view of the rocket taking off from directly below the primary boosters here.

Don't worry; tarantulas only attack if you show them you're sc-sc-scared.

My father's a taxman, actually.

I don't care if it does look like me; that voodoo doll's going straight down the waste-disposal unit.

All right, hand me the pliers, but I could have sworn the zookeeper said the rhinocerous should be *castigated*.

I'm just going to wrap a little cotton wool around that snake to stop it rattling.

Mike Tyson? Aren't you the one who –?

Go and show the old coach driver your scary Hallowe'en mask, son.

And you can prove you've got eight draws, darling: I kept the coupon.

Look, pretend *I'm* the clay pigeon ...

I think it said connect the brown wire to the negative terminal.

Just throw me that meat cleaver, would you?

Pick up those thirty-two empty lager cans, you lout!

No, darling, I'm sure they drive on the left over here in France.

Actually, there's a knack to opening these supersonic aeroplane windows.

You sure this firework's dead?

I rather fancy this cheese with the green mould on it.

Will you take a cheque, cabby?

Come outside and say that, Bruno.

Patchy fog? On this road! Don't make me la—.

Fancy a quick snifter before we leave Saudi?

Of coursh I'm frit to dive.

It says, 'Achtung! Minefield'. That's German for 'Welcome to Munich', isn't it?

We'll be safe enough on this motorway if we just follow that travelling salesman's Sierra.

See a doctor? Just for a ruptured aorta and a couple of dozen black suppurating pustules!

Whoops! Did I spill your scotch, McTavish?

These nuclear plants look lovely when they begin to glow like that, don't they?

Good Lord! It's not often a black cat causes you to break a mirror by crossing your path while you're walking under a ladder on Friday the 13th, is it?

Humpty Dumpty may sound like a daft name, but I know a safe wall when I see one.

The trick with a charging rhino is to stand perfectly still.

Two front berths on board the *Titanic*, please.

Give this juggernaut driver the V sign while we're overtaking him, would you, darling?

Well, here we are on the world's largest hydrogen airship: this calls for a cigarette.

Coo-er! Wait until I tell the missus I crashed into a car with an MAF 1A number plate!

Pass me a hanky; I'm going to wipe the foam off that dog's mouth.

So, this is Beirut.

"Hand me my City scarf... the lads are playing at Leeds today."

Readers wishing to visit Crinkley
Bottom are requested to contact the
Crinkley Bottom Tourist Officer.
He'd like a lift there himself, please.